Recipe
Collection

**Nutritious and delicious recipes
designed with your health in mind**

Published by foodworks4u, 90 High Street, Lewes BN7 1XN
Copyright ©Tina Deubert 2018
Website: www.foodworks4u.co.uk

ISBN 978-1-9993388-0-0

First published 2018

Designed by Antony Ashton - www.antonyashtonart.co.uk

Printed by Gemini Print Southern Ltd. on White UPM fine Offset

Contents

Thank you for buying my recipe collection

I hope you will turn to this book for your day to day cooking. Everything is simple to make, relatively quick, and endlessly variable, so I would love it if you took the recipes and made them your own, adapting to what is in season, what's in your cupboard and what you fancy.

These recipes have come about through a lifelong enjoyment of playing with food and creating in the kitchen, combined in more recent years with my understanding as a nutritional therapist. I love the challenge of taking someone's dietary needs and creating a dish they can enjoy, thrive on and repeat for themselves.

As I'm learning more about which foods nourish and benefit us, I'm constantly thinking about how to use them in a simple and tasty way, and the recipes in this book are some of the results of my explorations.

Tina's Kitchen is a small shop in Lewes, East Sussex, where I provide nutrient dense lunches designed to help balance blood sugar levels and avoid the mid-afternoon slump. All ingredients are organic except meat and fish, which is locally sourced. My aim is to help people feel better with good food, motivating them to want to eat well more often.

The daily menu consists of:

● Protein things like frittata, seedjacks, scotch eggs and hummus

● Five different salads using a range of dressings intended to support digestion and absorption

● Two stews, one vegan and one meat or fish

● Cakey things

This menu is represented in the four recipe sections of the book, which are preceded by a short store cupboard list and preparation tips. The recipes are followed by 'Nutritional Nuggets', nutritional benefits of some of the ingredients used in the recipes.

The final section is a nutritional information section called 'Nutrition in a nutshell', which explains the thinking behind my recipes in simple terms.

Why are there no photographs of the recipes?

I thought a lot about this, and realised that, because one of my main aims is to increase confidence and creativity, I want to communicate the fact that there is no set way a meal should look. If you are trying to imitate a beautiful food-styled photograph you may feel the recipe hasn't worked, even if it tastes wonderful.

This is home cooking – everyday stuff which you can put together quickly and easily. It therefore doesn't need to look like a restaurant meal, just attractively multi-coloured and tasty. I think that might be easier without a photo.

I really hope you enjoy making the food in this book and sharing it with friends and family.

Happy cooking,

Tina

Useful stuff to have in your kitchen

Here are some basic ingredients from which you can always make a meal.

NUTS & SEEDS
Nuts of all kinds – have a mixture
Flaked almonds can be useful
Sunflower, pumpkin, sesame, linseed/flax
Nut butter
Tahini (sesame seed paste)

SEASONINGS AND OIL
Olive oil
Cider vinegar
Olives
Tamarind paste
Tamari - wheat free soy sauce
Miso
Dried herbs e.g. oregano, thyme, rosemary, basil, bay leaves
Spices: e.g. ginger, turmeric, cumin, coriander, paprika, pepper, cinnamon
Bouillon powder or cubes
Dried fruits
Coconut: creamed/desiccated/milk

FRESH VEGETABLES & FRUITS
Avocadoes
Beetroot, carrots & other root veg
Fresh ginger and turmeric
Fresh herbs: parsley, chives, oregano, basil, mint
Green vegetables: kale, cabbage, broccoli, spinach etc
Lemons, limes & oranges
Lettuce/salad leaves (varied)
Onions, leeks & garlic
Sprouted seeds
Squashes
Sweet potatoes

CONVENIENCE FOODS
Dried beans and lentils (pulses)
Tinned pulses
Tinned fish (wild salmon, mackerel, sardines)
Eggs

FROZEN FOODS
Spinach
Peas
Fish and meat
Homemade bone stock (see p44)
Leftover veg
Berries

DAIRY
Organic cheeses
Butter
Natural live yogurt

This is a very simple list, most of which keeps well. There are no fancy ingredients, nothing too expensive, and nothing which isn't available in most decent supermarkets. Note that seeds are generally cheaper than nuts, while having similar nutritional properties.

Make sure you always have some green vegetables and vary the colours you serve alongside them. Consider getting an organic veg box; it gives you fresh, local, seasonal veg which may be new to you and can encourage you to try different things, widening your repertoire and increasing your nutrient intake. Getting a veg box creates a connection with the grower which helps us appreciate the effort that has gone into growing our food. We may then be more determined to use everything in the box, fridge and larder, which is good for our health, our purses, and our environment.

Preparation, tips and techniques

Vegetable preparation

I can understand that the idea of preparing vegetables is off-putting to many people, but there is no doubt they are an important part of a meal. You can chop and slice however you like – there is no correct way, but here are some suggestions, some of which make the job a bit easier and quicker.

Use as much of the veg as possible – use the green and white parts of leeks, just get rid of any manky-looking bits. Use the green parts of spring onions and the leaves of beetroot and turnips if you're lucky enough to get them. Green is good! Any slightly bitter taste is a great thing for our digestion and retraining our taste buds – you'll soon get used to it. The more you use, the more nutrition you're getting, the less you waste, and the further your money goes. It's win-win.

If you have a sensitive digestive system you may prefer to peel veg, but if not, why bother? There's a lot of goodness and fibre in and under the skin, so why waste time and effort peeling it and throwing it away? Give it a scrub to get rid of any mud, and remember that if you are cooking, the heat will destroy any germs, so you don't need to be too fastidious.

Do peel onions and garlic, swede and celeriac though – their skins may be high fibre but they won't be very palatable. Hard skinned squash will also need peeling.

There is no set way to prepare veg Sometimes you might want to slice carrots, sometimes cut them into little dice, or into batons/sticks; if they are small and young, you may want to use them whole – ring the changes for different textures and visual effects.

Onions can be sliced, diced, cut into chunks, or cooked whole, whatever you prefer and whatever fits with your meal.

Garlic can be crushed, chopped, or roasted whole and mashed.

If roasting veg, cut them into similar sized pieces so that they cook at the same rate, but if you are cooking a mixture, remember that denser vegetables like beetroot take longer to cook, so will need to be a bit smaller than less dense ones like celeriac or sweet potato.

Spinach can be chopped and mixed into just about any savoury dish – just give it a rinse (though if it's clean and going to be cooked it's not necessary) and chop it up. The same can be done with kale. As long as the stalks aren't too tough, chop them finely and always include them.

You can cook spinach very quickly by cutting it up, putting in a colander in the sink, then pouring freshly boiled water over it.

Broccoli – don't just eat the tree bits. The stalks are full of goodness and gut healthy fibre, so cut them up (slice, dice or sticks) and include them in whatever you're cooking, or dip into hummus.

Lemons, limes and oranges – I usually use the whole thing, including the pith and peel. Some recipes call for tiny slices. The method is:

- Cut the fruit in half from top to bottom

- Cut each half into four or five sections, lengthways

- Lay each section on a board, and with a sharp knife, cut into very thin slices to make little triangles

Pomegranates - cut them into quarters and gently turn inside out, holding them low in a wide bowl to catch any spurts of juice. Gently tease the seeds out into the bowl.

Always steam, stir-fry, oven cook or steam fry vegetables, rather than boil them (except ordinary potatoes) – you will retain more goodness, colour and flavour, and might even convert vegetable haters into vegetable lovers.

Beans and pulses

- Cook beans in bulk, cool and freeze them in portion sized bags or pots for another time. You can quickly defrost frozen beans by putting them in a bowl of hot water for a few minutes, without their bag or container.

- Don't add salt or tomato to the beans before they are properly soft, as this seems to harden the skins, making them less enjoyable to eat and possibly harder to digest.

You can buy many pulses in tins, and organic versions are not much more expensive than standard ones, so it's a handy store cupboard ingredient and worth keeping a selection of your favourites. Try to buy unsalted versions.

Soaking and cooking your own, however, has some advantages:

- Soaking pulses can begin to break down the 'anti-nutrients' which protect the seed from sprouting, making them easier to digest.

- Cooking them yourself means you can do a large batch and freeze them in portion sized bags, which is almost as convenient as a can.

- It is much cheaper.

- There is less packaging, which is better for the environment.

Soak the pulses in double their volume of cold water overnight but even a few hours is worth doing. Although it is possible to cook most lentils without soaking, it's still useful to do it if you have time.

It's often recommended that you cook in fresh water, but I tend to cook in the soaking water. It makes a good liquid for stews. Bring to the boil for at least 15 minutes, then reduce the heat so that the contents of the pan are gently bubbling and put a lid on. Take care that it doesn't boil over.

Cooking time varies. As a guide:

- Larger beans like chick peas, kidney beans and so on can take 1.5 to 2 hours.

- Split red lentils can cook in 30 minutes.

- Green and brown lentils take 30-60 minutes.

If the beans are taking longer, check that they are gently bubbling in the pan. You can also add ½ tsp bicarbonate of soda to the water which speeds up the cooking process.

You are aiming for a soft consistency – you don't want al dente beans as these are less palatable and harder to digest. Some beans can go mushy while others retain their shape.

My experience is that:

- Red lentils and mung beans go quite mushy, so they are good for things like dal, thickening stews, burgers, loaves and so on. They also make good hummus.

- Some of the brown, green and beluga lentils retain their shape quite well and can be used in salads as well as stews.

- Chick peas, kidney beans, pinto, butter beans and black-eyed beans generally retain their shape well. These tend to be the best ones to use for salad as well as stews.

Cooking beans in a slow cooker seems an attractive option, but the temperature doesn't get high enough. Pressure cookers are a great way to speed up the cooking time, and if you get one of the new electric ones, you can soak the beans and time the start of cooking, which is very convenient.

NOTE: Red kidney beans should always be boiled once for 15 minutes, the water then poured away, and then boiled in fresh water until cooked, to avoid the risk of food poisoning. The toxin present in red kidney beans can also be present in other beans (generally those of a similar shape) to a much lesser extent, so soaking for at least 5 hours and boiling vigorously for 15 minutes before turning the heat down is the best way to destroy the toxins.

Flavours

For me, a successful dish is one with layers of flavour. If a dish doesn't taste quite right I often feel it's lacking a bit of depth, so here are some taste tricks which might help:

- Try something sharp like pieces of lemon, lime, their juice or cider vinegar.

- A pinch of sea salt can just set the flavours off. Sea salt has useful amounts of trace minerals, whereas table salt is processed and contains very little. You actually need less sea salt because it is more flavoursome.

- Tamarind has a lovely taste which can add that final bit of depth. It is a useful addition to stews and sauces with its umami flavour - sweet, sour and something intense, which can just tip the balance and make a dish delicious. Tamarind is made from the pulp of a fruit and you buy it in jar.

- Miso can add a savoury, salty taste. This is fermented soya bean paste combined with barley (which contains gluten) or rice (which is gluten free).

If it's a sweeter taste you are after, try:

- Chopped apples, dates or other dried fruit

- Orange flesh

- Root vegetables – carrots, parsnips, sweet potato and beetroot for example

- Coconut – desiccated, creamed (block), milk or cream

- Cinnamon or vanilla essence

Do use herbs and spices as much as possible - they enhance the flavour and even tiny amounts have useful properties, some of which are listed in the Nutritional Nugget section.

All herbs and spices have beneficial properties, so, as with all your food, variety is key – just use them.

Remember to add nutrition not just flavour.

Nutritional equivalence

As well as tasting good, the food in this book is designed to be nutritionally dense, so if you don't fancy an ingredient, do try and swap it for something which is nutritionally equivalent – swap a herb for another herb or spice, a protein for a different protein, a vegetable for another vegetable, one type of fat for another, and so on.

Measurements

Most of these recipes don't require accurate measuring, so please don't get bogged down by it. The cakey things, seedjacks, beanjacks and cashew sauce are probably the only things which would be affected if you were too relaxed about it.

I've used tsp for teaspoon, dsp for dessertspoon and tbsp for tablespoon, which are approximately 5ml, 10ml and 15ml respectively.

I've suggested numbers of vegetables rather than weight, as that's much easier. If you feel you'd like more of something than I've suggested, do go ahead.

Saving energy

You'll notice the instruction to heat the oven doesn't come at the start of each recipe; this is because there is no point having an empty oven using up energy before it's needed. I've taken into account the preparation time and allowed about 10 minutes to heat the oven before it's needed.

On to the recipes...

Protein bits

Don't skip the protein part of your meal – it's arguably the most nutrient dense ingredient with an impressive list of benefits. I'm arguing for an adequate protein diet rather than a high protein one, and the simplest way to get this is to eat some protein with every meal and snack.

If you really need a snack, go for protein rather than carbohydrate or sweet things – you'll be doing yourself a big favour. Protein foods are generally more savoury than sweet, so choosing protein over sweet snacks can also help us retrain our taste buds.

Including protein with every meal can be a great way to improve blood sugar balancing and therefore mood and energy. It can also help reduce cravings for less desirable foods and support weight management.

Protein foods provide valuable nutrients which are harder to come by elsewhere, including important amino acids which provide the building blocks for our neurotransmitters (brain chemicals). Protein can therefore have a positive impact on mood and mental health.

Most of the following recipes can be included as part of a main meal or used as a snack or light meal on their own.

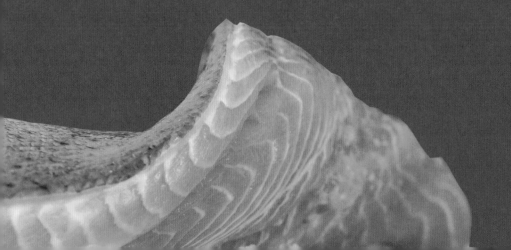

Protein Boosters

Here are some ideas for boosting the protein content of your meals, especially the meat free ones. If you are vegetarian or vegan it can be more of a challenge to get enough protein and a full range of amino acids in your diet. Have some of them ready-prepared in your cupboard or fridge and serve them at the table along with your food.

Mixed whole or ground nuts and seeds, used as a sprinkle on any meal – soup, salad, casseroles, cooked vegetables and so on.

Eggs are a fantastic protein food and contain all nutrients except vitamin C – a couple of eggs a day goes a long way to making sure you are getting a good level of protein in your diet. Try grated hard-boiled egg as a topping for just about anything or stir raw egg into a dish for the last minute of cooking.

Quinoa – use instead of rice or other grains as it is higher in protein and contains all the essential amino acids. It still needs nuts, seeds, eggs, cheese, meat, fish or pulses added to it, as the overall protein level is relatively low.

Remember that every little helps - it all adds up to provide a variety of nutrients.

Soaked nuts of any kind can be blended and used in smoothies, soups and stews to add a creamy texture and improve the protein content.

Gomasio – ground, toasted sesame seeds mixed with a small amount of sea salt. It's a great condiment and goes with many dishes. Dry fry 200g sesame seeds gently until they give off a lovely toasty smell. Grind them in a blender or coffee grinder with ½ tsp sea salt and some dried seaweed (optional). Once cool, put in a glass jar and keep in the fridge.

Tahini – (sesame seed paste) is a good source of protein, zinc, magnesium and calcium as well as B Vitamins. It makes soups and stews creamy and can be made into dressings or spreads.

Cashew Cream – Soak cashew nuts for 1-2 hours in water, drain, blend with enough water to cover.

Season, either with savoury seasonings like salt & pepper, garlic and herbs, or sweet, like cinnamon, dried fruit, desiccated coconut, vanilla or fresh lime.

Use to accompany any dish.

FRITTATA – basic recipe for 4 people

Frittata, basically a deep omelette, is one of the easiest and quickest meals you can make. It can be eaten for breakfast, lunch, dinner or as a snack, and you can include lots of vegetables to make it even more nutritious. You only need a frying pan, which you'll put under the grill to finish the top of the frittata.

Adapt this recipe according to ingredients you have and flavours you like. Variations follow. Cheese is generally salty, so you won't need salt if you're making a cheese version.

- 1-2 onions, sliced or chopped, as you prefer

- Olive oil - about 1 tbsp

- Greens of any kind – kale, spinach, broccoli, cabbage, whatever you have – about 2 handfuls when chopped

- 8 eggs

- Salt and pepper

- 1-2 tsp dried herbs or a handful of fresh chopped herbs

Pour the olive oil into the pan and gently fry the onions until translucent and beginning to turn brown at the edges.

Meanwhile beat the eggs in a bowl and add ½ tsp salt and a good ½ to 1 tsp freshly ground black pepper along with any herbs.

Add the greens to the pan and stir them until beginning to wilt. Pour this mixture into the eggs and stir in the bowl. (You can pour the egg straight into the pan, but I've found this way it is less likely to stick – not guaranteed though!)

Put a little more oil in the pan if you're not confident about its non-stick qualities then pour in the egg mixture. Cook over a low heat until the egg is mostly set.

Heat the grill, place the pan under the grill and cook to finish, until it has turned a light golden brown. Allow to settle for a few minutes in the pan before serving.

If you have a good pan (I find stainless steel works best and I avoid non-stick coatings), you may be able to slide the whole thing out of the pan and onto a serving plate. If not, cut it into portions while in the pan, taking care not to scratch the bottom, then lift each piece out using a slice.

Variations

Beetroot or sweet potato and feta cheese
Grate a medium beetroot/sweet potato and cook with the onions. You can also use diced cooked beetroot (boiled or roasted).

Dice about 30g feta cheese per person and add to the egg mix. Continue as before.

Sweet potato and mushroom
Cut sweet potato into small dice, slice the mushrooms and fry both with the onions until the sweet potato is soft. Stir in a couple of teaspoons of dried oregano then continue as before.

Feta, pea/broad bean and mint
Use frozen peas/broad beans, 30g diced feta per person and fresh mint or a little mint sauce.

Salmon or other fish
Cut into small pieces and add once the onions are translucent. When the fish is cooked through, add some lemon zest or lemon dressing (see page 26), then continue as before. Dill goes nicely with this, fresh or dried. Make a luxury salmon version with the inclusion of cream cheese and fresh dill.

Any cheese
Add 30g per person of your favourite cheese, diced or grated, to the egg mix.

Breakfast frittata
Fry mushrooms with the onions, add blue cheese (or other) to the egg mix and top with little pieces of bacon, ham, tomatoes etc.

Blue cheese, celery & walnut
Add some chopped celery to the onions, a handful of walnuts and around 150g blue cheese to the egg mixture. Top with more walnuts if desired.

Pumpkin seed and pesto
Mix 2 dsp good quality pesto with the beaten eggs, add about 100g pumpkin seeds to the pan with the greens then proceed as before, topping the frittata with more pumpkin seeds.

Moroccan inspired frittata
Cook about 150g minced lamb with the onions, then add a drained tin of kidney beans, ½ - 1 tsp each cinnamon, paprika, cumin, coriander and chilli (optional), a handful of sultanas or chopped dried apricots (optional).

Add imagination and create your own version.

MINI FRITTATA (makes 12)

We make our mini frittata using silicone muffin trays. They are great for snacks, little nibbles or party food, and you can add whatever ingredients you like to them.

Heat the oven to 180°C/350°F/Gas 4.

Remember to lay the silicone tray onto a metal tray before filling it up if it's one of the floppy ones.

Simply chop an onion and some other vegetables – try spinach or kale, grated carrot or beetroot, add about a tablespoon chopped olives or sun-dried tomatoes and some cheese of your choice. You want enough veg to half fill each muffin hole, and the egg fills the rest of the space.

Beat 9 large eggs, add your veg mix and pour into the muffin holes. Bake in the oven for 25-30 minutes until lightly browned. Wait a minute or two before removing from the tray and cool on a rack.

You can also chop up vegetables and protein, pop them in the muffin holes and pour the egg on top – it works just as well and could be a great activity with children, allowing them to choose their own ingredients.

Variations

- Pesto and pumpkin seed or pine nuts/flaked almonds/toasted hazelnuts
- Feta and grated beetroot, carrot or sweet potato
- Sheep or goat cheese and olives or sun-dried tomatoes
- Good quality ham and cheese
- Mushroom and sweet potato

HUMMUS

The easiest way to make hummus is to use tinned organic chickpeas but soaking dried chickpeas overnight and boiling them yourself is cheaper and could make the them more digestible (see notes on page 7 about cooking pulses for more information). Remember that you can make hummus with any bean, so do experiment – although authentic hummus is made with chickpeas, rules are there to be broken!

For me, hummus is a regular part of a salad meal – a big dollop or two makes a great addition. We've got used to dipping breads and crisps into it, but do enjoy it spread on little gem lettuce, thin slices of beetroot, turnip or other root vegetables, on a salad or as a dip with veg. Personally, I don't like bready things with hummus, as it feels too starchy; I feel crisp, fresh vegetables complement the texture and taste of hummus better. It also keeps the carbs lower, as pulses contain plenty of carbohydrate.

More tahini than usual, whole lemon and extra virgin olive oil makes this hummus much more nutrient dense than shop-bought versions.

- 1 whole organic lemon and 1-2 tbsp olive oil OR 2 tbsps lemon dressing (page 26)

- 1 drained can or 250g (cooked weight) home cooked chick peas or beans

- 1-3 cloves of garlic

- 2 tbsp tahini

- Salt to taste (½ to 1 tsp)

- Water if necessary to loosen the mixture

Chop the whole lemon (peel and all) roughly, peel the garlic and put into a food processor or other machine with the olive oil. You can also use a stick blender.

Blend until you have a paste with a thickness like Greek yogurt. Add more oil if needed.

Add the rest of the ingredients except the water, and blend again until you have a texture you like, adding a little water if it's too thick. Taste and adjust the seasoning.

Hummus Variations

- Use different beans – experiment with cannellini, mung beans, butter beans, red or black beans, pinto beans and fava beans (dried broad beans) for different tastes and textures.

- Ditch the beans and try soaked sunflower seeds and pumpkin seeds instead for higher protein and good fats. Soak the seeds overnight in water, drain and use instead of chick peas. Use fresh water to loosen the mixture as needed. This has a coarser texture than usual.

- Add a vegetable or herb to bump up the nutritional value – roast carrot, grated beetroot, spinach, avocado, parsley, coriander, fresh turmeric etc.

- Black beans, lime and ginger.

- Any light coloured beans with fresh turmeric and coriander.

SEEDJACKS (makes 10-12)

This is a signature Tina's Kitchen recipe – it works as a snack, a meal on the go and even as nibbles with drinks. Each full-sized seedjack contains 15-17g of protein, which is a decent contribution to your daily needs. It comes out like a round flapjack.

Blood sugar balancing is key to many aspects of health, and the humble seedjack is a great way to support steady blood sugar and avoid the highs and lows which can make us feel so bad.

You'll find one seedjack can act as breakfast or a convenient lunch or snack when you haven't got time to eat 'properly'. Seedjacks are a good way of incorporating some vegetables and fibre without it being obvious.

You can also make a cheese-free version (see variations).

Don't worry if you haven't got the four seeds listed, just use what you have; I find hemp seeds are a bit sandy in texture so personally I don't use them.

You can use any vegetables except 'wet' ones like tomatoes, as you want a crispy texture when the seedjacks are cooked.

Grease or line a couple of large baking trays with parchment paper or a silicone baking sheet.

- 400g chopped or grated mixed vegetables (cooked or raw, so you can use leftovers). No need to peel them, simply scrub. If you have a food processor you can chop them coarsely in the machine.

- 400g mixed seeds (sesame, sunflower, linseed and pumpkin)

- 400g grated cheese (we use organic cheddar but do experiment – feta works well too)

- 3 eggs

Mix the chopped veg, seeds and cheese together in a large bowl, then add the eggs and mix well with a wooden spoon or your hands.

Heat the oven to 180°C/350°F/Gas 4.

Divide your mixture into 10-12 balls and arrange them on your trays, flattening them with your hands until about 1cm thick. Leave some space between them, as they will spread out a bit. As a guide, our uncooked seedjacks weigh 130g each and fill a 100ml measuring pot but do make them any size.

Place in the oven and bake for 10 minutes, then flatten them further with a metal slice.

Return to the oven for a further 20-30 minutes until golden brown.

Cool on a rack.

They can be eaten slightly warm or cold, and freeze well.

Variations

- Make a dairy free version with more egg, some ground flax or pea flour (to help them stick together) and some seasoning (salt, pepper and herbs).

- Make mini seedjacks for parties or for children, by dividing into much smaller balls.

- Add curry spices to make them taste like pakora.

BEANJACKS

This is a useful bread substitute as well as a nutritious snack. It's simple to make, keeps in the fridge for about a week and freezes well – which is great because this recipe makes 24. To make less, just halve the ingredients. If you haven't got all the seeds, just use what you have, but you do need at least 100g of flax/linseed as this helps stick them together – as always, experiment and adjust according to what's available. It works with carrot as well as beetroot, so do try other root vegetables.

Beanjacks are a slow releasing, high nutrient food containing a useful 4g of protein each, making a valuable addition to meat-free meals.

Cover 2 large baking trays with parchment paper or silicone sheets.

- 400g beetroot (can be raw or cooked)
- 400g mixed ground seeds (pumpkin, sunflower, sesame and linseed) – use a coffee grinder to grind them to a coarse sand texture
- 1 drained tin of black beans (240g cooked weight)
- 1 tsp salt

Whizz the beans and beetroot with the salt in a food processor until mushy. Alternatively, grate the beetroot finely and mash the beans, then mix together.

In a large bowl, mix the mash and ground seeds together with your hands and divide into 24 balls.

Heat the oven to 180°C/350°F/Gas 4

Put some water in a small bowl for wetting your hands. Using wet hands, arrange the balls on the trays and flatten them into rounds a little bigger than an oatcake. Keep wetting your hands as needed. Smooth the tops with a circular motion using the heel of your hand and smooth any jagged edges. These don't spread out, so you can place them fairly close together on the tray. You may need to bake in two batches.

Bake for 20-25 minutes then put onto a cooling rack. They are done when they feel firm to the touch (lift the edge of one to feel).

Scotch eggs are great – they can be a high quality, high protein snack which is so satisfying it can act as a convenient meal and keep you going for hours. Here are two versions - a veggie one and a lamb one. Both are delicious.

MUSHROOM SCOTCH EGGS

This veggie version works much better than the lentil-clad options you usually get; the covering is so delicious I think it would even work as a bread. It is equally loved by meat eaters and vegetarians.

- 4 eggs, to hard boil

- 1 raw egg, for coating

- 200g mushrooms

- 200g grated cheese

- 300g ground mixed seeds, including at least 75g linseeds (flax) as they help to stick the mixture together

- 1 tsp black pepper

- 1 tbsp ground almonds and 1 tbsp coconut flour for coating

Boil the eggs – cover with water, bring to the boil, and once bubbling, put the lid on and turn off the heat – by the time you're ready, they will be cooked.

Chop the mushrooms finely in a food processor, add the cheese and seeds and mix well until you have a sausage meat like texture. If you haven't got a food processor, you can grate the mushrooms – it works fine.

Heat the oven to 180°C/350°F/Gas 4 and prepare a baking tray, greased or lined with parchment paper or a silicone mat.

On a plate, mix together the ground almonds and coconut flour with a little pepper (this is the coating). Beat the raw egg in a separate dish, big enough to dip a completed Scotch egg in.

●●●

Lay out the following things on your work surface:

- Scotch egg mix divided into 4 equal lumps

- Flour mix on a plate

- Beaten egg in a flattish bowl

- Peeled hard boiled eggs

- Baking tray, oiled or covered with a silicone or parchment paper sheet

Flatten a lump of Scotch egg mix, dip a peeled egg into the flour mix, then wrap the mushroom mix round the outside, sealing it well and making it smooth and round. This is a very satisfying job – enjoy the process and be proud of your lovely round Scotch egg.

Dip the Scotch egg into raw egg then roll in the flour and place on the baking sheet. Do the same for all of them, then bake in the oven for 30-40 minutes.

They are done when they appear nicely browned. Put onto a cooling rack, carefully, as they are soft when hot, and allow to cool to room temperature before eating. They solidify as they cool.

LAMB SCOTCH EGGS

This Persian inspired version using cashew nuts, dates and spices, is a great alternative to the standard pork and rusk mixture, which can be a bit dry.

- 4 eggs to hard boil

- 1 raw egg for the coating

- 50g dates

- 75g cashew nuts

- 1 medium onion, finely chopped

- 300g minced lamb

- ½ tsp salt

- ¾ tsp cinnamon

- 1.5 tsp ground cumin

- 1.5 tsp ground coriander

- ¾ tsp black pepper

- 1tbsp ground almonds and 1 tbsp coconut flour for coating (I've used each of these on their own, so use whatever you have)

Boil the eggs – cover with water, bring to the boil, and once bubbling, put the lid on and turn off the heat – by the time you're ready, they will be cooked.

In a food processor, chop the dates finely and tip them into a mixing bowl. Do the same with the cashew nuts and onions, tipping them into the same bowl.

Add the minced lamb, spices, salt and pepper to the bowl and mix everything together well.

Divide into 4 equal portions.

Heat the oven to 180°C/350°F/Gas 4 and prepare a baking tray, greased or lined with parchment paper or a silicone mat.

On a plate, mix together the ground almonds and coconut flour with a little pepper (this is the coating). Beat the raw egg in a separate dish, big enough to dip a completed Scotch egg in.

Lay out the following things on your work surface:

- Scotch egg mix divided into 4 equal lumps

- Flour mix on a plate

- Beaten egg in a flattish bowl

- Peeled hard boiled eggs

- Baking tray, oiled or covered with a silicone or parchment paper sheet

Flatten a lump of Scotch egg mix, dip a peeled egg into the flour mix, then wrap the mix round the egg, sealing it well and making it smooth and round. This is a satisfying job – enjoy the process and be proud of your lovely round Scotch egg.

Dip the Scotch egg into raw egg then roll in the flour and place on the baking sheet.

Do the same for all of them, then bake in the oven for 30-40 minutes. They are done when they appear nicely browned. Cool on a rack and enjoy warm or cold.

NUT ROAST

This is a simple and delicious nut loaf, loved by vegetarians and meat eaters alike. The following recipe makes a standard loaf tin, or you can use muffin tins to make mini versions. Ring the changes with the nuts and seeds, try blue cheese, other cheeses or no cheese with a bit more egg and seasoning.

Heat the oven to 170°C/325°F/Gas 3 and line a loaf tin with parchment paper.

- 120g each cashew nuts, almonds and sunflower seeds (total 360g)

- Olive oil

- 2-3 onions, chopped

- 2-3 leeks, sliced, including the green bits

- 3-4 sticks of celery, sliced finely

- 150g grated cheese (cheddar works well, but try feta or blue cheese)

- 2 eggs

- 3-4 tsp bouillon powder or ½-1 tsp salt (to taste)

- 1 tsp dried thyme

- 1 tsp ground black pepper

Roughly chop the nuts and seeds in a food processor (use the 'pulse' setting so that it doesn't get too fine), into gravel sized pieces.

In a large saucepan, heat the olive oil and fry the onions, leeks and celery gently until softened. Turn off the heat.

Add the seasoning and herbs, stir, then add the chopped nuts and grated cheese.

Mix well, taste it and adjust the seasoning, then add the eggs, and tip the mixture into the prepared loaf tin.

Bake for 35-40 minutes until nicely browned on the top.

Allow to settle for a few minutes before removing from the tin to serve.

This tastes just as good cold and freezes well. You can freeze it either before baking or once it's cooked.

MEAT AND CHICKEN LIVER PATTIES

You can ring the changes with this, using different meats and seasonings. Bake them in the oven as individual burgers or in a tin as a meat loaf. You can also gently shallow fry them.

- 1 medium onion, finely chopped

- 250g chicken, lamb or beef mince

- 100g organic chicken liver

- ½ tsp dried rosemary or thyme

- ½ tsp black pepper

- ½ tsp salt

- Zest of 1 lemon

Heat the oven to 170°C/325°F/Gas 3

Mix everything together in a mixing bowl and shape into 5 or 6 little burgers or patties.

Place on an oiled baking tray, muffin moulds or Yorkshire pudding tins and bake in the oven for 30-40 minutes or fry them gently in a pan.

Salad Dressings

As well as top quality organic ingredients, it's the dressings which make our salads special. Adding just the right flavours can really make the difference between a mediocre salad and a delicious one with lots of depth and layers of taste.

Tina's Kitchen dressings have nutritional benefits as well as enhancing the taste of the vegetables.

You'll notice there is no sweetener in any of these dressings; it's become the norm to sweeten dressings, making even our savoury foods taste sweet! There's no doubt that getting away from this habit is a major step in our journey to better health, so do learn to enjoy the more complex flavours you'll notice without the sweetness.

Tip: Use a permanent marker on a glass jar to note the type of dressing and the date and store in the fridge – it will scrub off later when you wash up the jar.

The dressings which follow can be made in a reasonable quantity and stored in a jar in the fridge, so once you've made them, you can brighten up any salad.

BASIC CIDER VINEGAR & OLIVE OIL

The simplest dressings are quick and easy, yet still enhance your vegetables. Use live cider vinegar and good quality extra virgin olive oil and simply splash onto your salad – no need to mix it in advance.

Whizzed Citrus Dressings

The following four dressings are all made in a similar way – whole, organic citrus whizzed with olive oil and flavourings.

LEMON DRESSING

Wash and cut a whole organic lemon into pieces (you can even leave the pips in).

Put into a food processor, blender or similar machine and cover with an equal volume of olive oil. Blend until smoothish. The consistency will vary according to the lemon – whether it's juicy and how soft the skin is – and your machine.

Vary it by adding garlic, parsley, coriander or other herbs and spices.

Use this for dressing beetroot, carrot and other root vegetables, bitter leaves like chicory and radicchio, making hummus and on fish, chicken or other meat – it seems to go with anything.

Store in a glass jar in the fridge; it can keep for several weeks.

LIME AND GINGER DRESSING

Use a couple of soft skinned* limes instead of lemon, a thumb sized piece of fresh ginger (no need to peel if it's organic), and olive oil.

Prepare and use in the same way as lemon dressing. It goes very well with a slaw and complements beetroot beautifully, especially when roasted.

*If your limes have gone a bit hard, cut the skins off with a sharp knife and just use the flesh.

Store in a glass jar; it will keep for about a week.

ORANGE AND ANISEED DRESSING

This is a lovely dressing which we use on grated raw swede. It also goes very well with beetroot, celeriac, carrot and fennel.

Make it just like the lemon dressing, using a whole orange instead and add ¼ tsp ground aniseed and the juice of a whole lemon or 1 dsp cider vinegar.

Store in a glass jar; it will keep for about a week.

MOROCCAN STYLE DRESSING

Blitz 2 limes and olive oil in a liquidiser or similar (as with the lemon dressing).

Add:

- 1.5 tsp ground cumin
- 1.5 tsp ground coriander
- 1 tsp cinnamon
- 2 tsp paprika
- 2 tsp dried dill or fresh dill leaves
- ½ tsp salt
- 1 tsp black pepper

The following dressings are mixed by hand in a jug or bowl

MUSTARD DRESSING

Use this with any brassica salad – broccoli, cabbage, Brussels sprouts, kale and so on. It enhances the nutritional value of these superfoods and makes their magic qualities more available to the body.

- 1 tbsp wholegrain mustard

- 1 tbsp each black and yellow mustard seeds (optional)

- 2 tbsp cider vinegar

- 2 tbsp extra virgin olive oil

Mix everything by shaking it in a sealed glass jar.

This keeps for several weeks in the fridge.

MISO DRESSING

Using fermented, unpasteurised miso means you are including some beneficial bacteria in your dressing.

This goes well with any slaw and should keep for at least a week in the fridge.

Mix 1 tsp miso with some olive oil and cider vinegar. Add lime, soy sauce, ginger, garlic, fresh coriander and/or chilli, depending on what you have and what you fancy. Taste the dressing and alter the seasoning to taste.

TAHINI DRESSING

This is a great dressing for raw kale salad and goes with other brassica (cabbage) family vegetables, as well as veggie or meat burgers and many other things.

- 1 tbsp tahini

- 2 tbsp water

- 2 tsp soy sauce or more (Tamari is wheat free)

- 1 clove of garlic, crushed

- 1 tsp finely grated fresh ginger

Mix the tahini and water together in a bowl or jug first – it takes a while, but all of a sudden turns a paler coloured, smooth mixture like double cream.

Add the rest of the ingredients, mix well and adjust the taste if you wish.

Try adding some fresh turmeric along with the ginger for extra antioxidant and anti-inflammatory properties.

You can also make a very simple version with just tahini, water and soy sauce.

It will keep for about a week in a glass jar in the fridge.

AVOCADO AND BASIL DRESSING

Simply whizz or mash a ripe avocado with olive oil, lemon or lime (peel on or off), some fresh basil and season with salt and pepper. This works well with raw courgette, and also as a dressing for fish, meat and other proteins.

It needs to be used the day it's made.

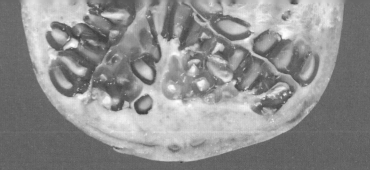

Salads

There are many combinations of vegetables which make great salads with the dressings in the previous section. What follows is a brief description of some of the salads we make at Tina's Kitchen.

They are suggestions only – once you get into the swing of it, please chop and change, mix and match, according to what is in season and what you have in your cupboard or fridge.

I don't generally use the nightshade family (tomatoes, peppers, aubergines and potatoes) because in some people they can promote inflammation. Bear in mind that conditions like rosacea and arthritis may respond well to nightshade-free diets. There's some thought that this family could also increase symptoms of heartburn. If you have any kind of inflammatory issue, consider cutting out the nightshade family for a month and see how you feel.

Part of the problem with tomatoes in particular could be that we eat them all year round, often slightly unripe, which means they have higher quantities of tomatine, a chemical thought to increase inflammation.

Apart from that, EVERYONE uses tomatoes and peppers all the time, and potatoes are also ubiquitous, so as I'm keen to give people fresh ideas, I want to show that you can have delicious and more varied salads without them.

On the following pages are some of the combinations we make.

There are suggestions for how to prepare, but in general, it's nice to have similar sized pieces in a salad; consider what you would like to have on a fork – I think it's nice to get a mixture of flavours and textures.

Also remember that we are aiming to 'eat a rainbow' every day, so look at the colours of the vegetables you are using and think about how lovely it will look on your plate. Make an edible work of art and enjoy the process.

Some useful ingredients to put in salads:

- Avocado
- Artichokes
- Beetroot
- Broccoli
- Cabbage
- Carrots
- Cauliflower
- Celeriac
- Celery
- Chicory
- Cooled roasted vegetables: sweet potato, squash, root veg, courgettes, cauliflower…
- Fennel
- Frozen peas
- Kale
- Olives
- Onions
- Radicchio
- Sprouted seeds
- Swede (yes, raw swede)
- Turnips (they are delicious raw)
- Apples
- Dried fruit (moderate amounts)
- Lemons
- Oranges
- Pears
- Pomegranate
- Nuts and seeds
- Tinned or home cooked beans and pulses
- Fresh and dried herbs and spices
- Fresh turmeric and ginger

BEAN SALAD

This will keep well in the fridge for 3 or 4 days, so can provide a good base for packed lunches.

If you are cooking your own beans, once they are ready, cool them in cold water briefly, then drain them. Adding warmish beans to the dressing will help them absorb more of the flavours, and leaving it for some time will improve the flavour even more.

Make the dressing first, then soak the chopped onions and garlic in it for an hour or more, even overnight – this softens the taste of raw onions and makes them more digestible.

● 1 or 2 tins, or 250-500g cooked beans (eg black beans, red beans, white, chick peas) – a mixture looks good and works well

● 2 tbsps each of cider vinegar & olive oil

● 1-2 red onions, chopped or sliced finely

● 1-2 cloves garlic, crushed

● ½ tsp salt

● 1 tsp oregano, thyme, rosemary or basil

● ½ tsp pepper

● 2-4 sticks of celery

● Large bunch parsley

Dressing - Put the oil, vinegar, salt, pepper and oregano into a bowl or jug. Chop the onion fairly finely (red onions work well and look pretty, but white is also fine) and put this into the dressing with the crushed garlic. Leave to soak.

Salad - Add the beans to the dressing and stir to mix. You can leave this mixture soaking and add the celery and parsley later if you wish. Finely slice the celery, chop the parsley (remember to use the stalks, cut finely) and add this to the bean mixture.

Taste and adjust the seasoning.

Roast Vegetable Salads

Roasting vegetables is great, because you can enjoy them hot with a meal, then in your lunch, or freeze leftovers for use another time in a soup or stew.

You can roast any veg; just cut into bite sized pieces, add oil, seasoning, herbs or spices, onions and leeks. You don't need to cook at high temperatures – a medium oven is fine. Food cooked at high temperatures can become damaged, which is not so good for us.

CAULIFLOWER, LEEKS, CURRY SPICES

Cut the cauliflower into fork sized pieces, toss in olive oil, spices (e.g. cumin, coriander or curry powder), salt and pepper, taste and adjust the seasoning, then cook for 15 minutes (it is also good raw just like this). Stir through some chopped spinach or kale at the end. Spinach will be cooked by the heat of the cauliflower, and if you use kale it just needs a couple of minutes back in the oven.

SQUASH

Any kind – with onions and leeks, herbs of your choice, chilli or curry spices, olive oil, salt and pepper.

SWEET POTATO, LEEKS, ONIONS, ROSEMARY AND THYME

Scrub the potatoes, cut into fork-sized chunks, season with herbs, salt and pepper and coat lightly with olive oil. It takes around 30-40 minutes. You can also stir through some greens at the end.

BEETROOT - two ways

Scrub and cut into fork-sized chunks, then choose one of these:

- Roast with olive oil, salt and pepper, cool, then stir in the lime and ginger dressing on page 27, finishing it off with chopped fresh coriander.

- Roast with finely sliced lemon, olive oil, salt, pepper and dill seeds.

PARSNIP AND GINGER

Scrub and cut up the parsnips, grate a good amount of fresh ginger (for 1kg parsnips use 30-50g ginger) and mix this with olive oil, salt and pepper. Taste the dressing; add more pepper or salt if necessary. Coat the parsnips and cook for 30-40 minutes. Add fresh coriander or something green at the end.

MIXED ROOTS

Beetroot, carrot, celeriac, swede, parsnips...
Choose herbs you like, dill or caraway seeds,
salt and pepper, perhaps finely slice a
lemon and mix with olive oil.
Stir something green in at the end
to set off all the colours beautifully.

Brassica Salads

Brassica, or cruciferous vegetables, are all those belonging to the cabbage family and include broccoli, kale, cauliflower, cabbage, turnip, radish, swede, chard, kohlrabi, Brussels sprouts, rocket, mustard leaves, pak choi and watercress.

All have health benefits, so including them daily is a great way to support your body's detoxification processes and possibly help reduce your risk of cancer. Research shows reduced bowel cancer risk in those who eat brassicas regularly.

Here are some of the brassica family salads we make. Do mix and match and come up with your own versions. Remember to enjoy the process of making a beautiful salad.

BROCCOLI, SPROUTED SEEDS AND POMEGRANATE

One of my favourites. This salad can look very beautiful – the pomegranate is well worth the effort, so do allow a bit of time; there are 'quick' ways of removing the seeds, but they invariably damage them and make a big mess, so I think it's worth the extra effort. It's like a little bit of meditation in your day. Please see page 7 for a tip on how to prepare.

Cut the stalk off the broccoli, divide the head into individual florets (trees) and slice them so that you get little tree shaped pieces. You may need to cut some of these in half. This sounds fiddly, but looks beautiful; you can just slice through the head if you're in a hurry.

DO USE THE STALK! If the outer layer is tough, you can literally peel it off with a knife. The inside is full of goodness, and tastes delicious, so slice it thinly or cut lengthways then into sticks and include in your salad. Put the tougher bits into your seedjacks (page 16).

Rinse a pack of any sprouted seeds and gently remove the jewel-like seeds from the pomegranate.

Mix everything together gently with the mustard dressing on page 28 and serve.

Variations: Add finely sliced cabbage, radicchio, chicory, fennel or cauliflower (prepared in the same way as broccoli), and if you are really short of time skip the pomegranates and substitute blackberries, dried cherries, cranberries or blueberries. It will still work without these and have plenty of benefits.

CAULIFLOWER AND FENNEL SALAD

My plan was to make a lightly roasted salad (you can do that, too), but the mix was left, prepared, in the fridge overnight and we discovered it was delicious raw.

Cut up cauliflower, first into florets, then tree-shaped cross sections. Remember to use the stalks as well, cut into little sticks.

Finely slice fennel. Mix with lemon juice and olive oil, a little salt and some fennel seeds. Cut up half a lemon into segments then tiny, thin slices (see page 7) and mix everything together.

BRUSSELS SPROUT AND PARSNIP SALAD

This is cooked and allowed to cool before using as a salad.

Mix raw Brussels and scrubbed, cut up parsnips with red onion and very finely sliced orange, olive oil, salt and pepper. Roast in a medium oven for about 20-30 minutes and cool before adding cider vinegar, hazelnuts and pomegranate.

RAW BRUSSELS SPROUT SALAD

Wash, remove any grotty outer leaves, then thinly slice raw sprouts. Mix with either the mustard dressing or a basic cider vinegar and olive oil dressing, season with salt and pepper, and add some chopped hazelnuts.

Optional extras:
Red onion, pomegranate, very finely sliced orange (including the skin), sprouted seeds, fresh herbs.

RAW KALE AND TAHINI SALAD

At its most basic, this is simply kale with the tahini dressing on page 29.

Wash and shred the kale finely, including as much of the stalk as possible. Massage the dressing in with your hands, which helps soften the kale. Variations could include added carrot, kohlrabi, swede or beetroot cut into sticks or grated, pomegranate seeds, sesame seeds, broccoli or other sprouts. The tahini dressing works really well with this, but do try other dressings as well.

SLICED TURNIP WITH MOROCCAN STYLE DRESSING AND POMEGRANATE

This is a surprising salad. Most people eat turnips cooked, which can be uninspiring, so try them raw – they are crunchy and delicious; in my opinion they should only be used this way. Slices of turnip are also great vehicles for spreads and hummus. Use the Moroccan style dressing on page 27.

- 500g fresh turnips, with leaves if possible

- 1 medium red onion

- 1 pomegranate

- Green stuff (turnip leaves, watercress, spinach)

Wash the turnips. Leave the peel on as it is very pretty and, as always, peel contains valuable nutrients.

Cut the turnips into quarters then slice thinly so that you get little triangular shapes, then finely slice the onion.

Carefully remove the seeds from the pomegranate.

Wash the green leaves, and chop roughly. Combine everything gently with the dressing and serve.

Slaws

Slaw is basically a cabbage salad, and you can vary it enormously, depending on what's in season and what you have in your fridge. A slaw is a great way of incorporating a lot of different raw vegetables into one salad, so it can be a very useful lunchbox salad or simple accompaniment to meat, fish or other protein foods.

Cabbage goes with many different dressings; forget the ubiquitous mayonnaise that goes into coleslaw and try some of the following (the recipes are on pages 26-29).

- Mustard dressing

- Lime and ginger dressing

- Orange and aniseed dressing

- Miso dressing

- Tahini dressing – this may look a bit messy, but tastes lovely

- Lemon dressing

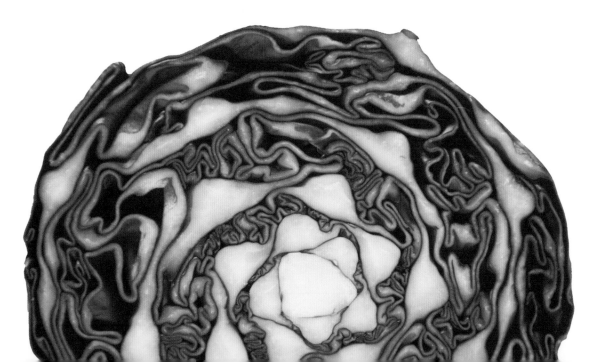

MIXED CABBAGE, MUNG BEAN SPROUTS AND CORIANDER

Using fresh coriander, finely shredded white, green and red cabbage, mung bean sprouts and perhaps some dried seaweed.

- You can also add some sesame, pumpkin and/or sunflower seeds.
- Try with the mustard dressing, lime and ginger or the miso dressing.

WHITE/GREEN CABBAGE AND APPLE

Thinly slice an apple with the skin on, pop it straight into lemon juice or cider vinegar, mix with shredded cabbage and use lime and ginger, lemon or mustard dressing.

RED CABBAGE & CELERIAC

Finely slice or grate red cabbage, grate peeled celeriac and mix with any lemony dressing; it goes a beautiful pink colour and is delicious.

RAINBOW SLAW

Use any cabbage, grated carrot, fine sticks of kohlrabi, radish or swede, beetroot, finely chopped onion (or spring onions), sprouted seeds, celeriac, celery, fresh parsley or coriander.

Finely slice the cabbage and grate the root vegetables. Add some apple or finely chopped dried fruit if you wish, maybe some seeds. Any of the dressings will work well.

FENNEL AND APPLE

Finely slice fennel bulbs and apples (peel on), include any frondy bits from the fennel, add a teaspoon of fennel seeds if you have them, and mix with either the lemon dressing or the orange and aniseed. This also works well with cider vinegar and olive oil.

COURGETTE WITH AVOCADO DRESSING

Slice or cut raw, fresh courgettes into strips and mix with the avocado dressing on page 29. Garnish with some fresh basil.

CHICORY, RADICCHIO AND POMEGRANATE

This is one of my favourites. The bitter flavours of these leaves are balanced by the sharp sweetness of the pomegranate and the surprising creaminess of the lemon dressing.

Simply cut the radicchio and chicory finely, as if you were making a slaw, carefully remove the seeds from a pomegranate, then gently mix with the lemon dressing. Add sprouted seeds if you wish.

ROOT VEGETABLE SALADS

Some suitable dressings for root veg are:

- Lemon dressing, page 26
- Lime & ginger dressing, page 27
- Orange & aniseed dressing, page 27
- Miso dressing, page 28

Grated carrot

With lemon dressing and poppy seeds or sesame seeds – add enough seeds to create an attractive speckling throughout the salad. Add fresh parsley or coriander if you have some. You could also add chopped hazelnuts, sunflower, sesame or pumpkin seeds.
Carrot also goes well with lime and ginger or orange and aniseed dressings.

Grated raw swede

Try this with the orange and aniseed dressing – it's surprisingly delicious. You will need to peel swede.

Beetroot and carrot

Scrub and grate equal quantities of these two amazingly coloured vegetables and mix with any of the citrus dressings. Lemon is the staple for me, but the others go equally well.

Beetroot and apple

Put some cider vinegar in a bowl, cut the apple into little slices (peel on), grate the raw beetroot and mix together with a splash of olive oil.

Mixed roots

Scrub and grate beetroot and carrot, peel and grate swede and celeriac. Mix together with the lemon or orange dressing – it looks really pretty and tastes wonderful.

Stews

Stews are one pot wonders – you can put everything into the pot and simply steam some greens to accompany it later.

At Tina's Kitchen all stews are served without rice, potatoes or bread because they are complete meals in themselves, and part of my mission is to plant the seed in people's minds that you don't need starch to make a meal. The use of beans and pulses gives you complex, nutrient dense carbohydrates as well as vegetable protein and fibre, which means slower energy release, improved blood sugar balance and therefore steady energy and mood, as well as easier weight management and reduction of cravings.

All the stews which follow can be made vegan or with meat, so follow the instructions and use meat if you want to and leave it out if you don't. Suggested meats are in brackets after the title. Make a veggie version by doubling the pulses and using a vegetable stock.

Do remember that pulses contain about half the protein of meat and fish, so you will need to add more protein (see Protein Boosters on page 11).

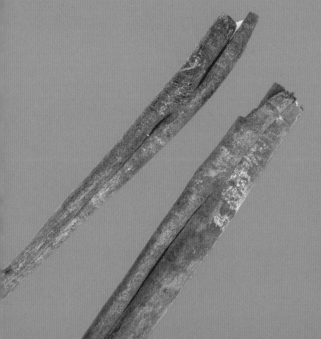

Meat stews are usually made with a basic bone stock as their liquid, which increases nutritional value. Vegetarian stews can be made with a simple vegetable stock or water. Both stock instructions follow on the next page.

It's important to make sure stews are substantial – they are definitely not soups, which are often more of a drink than a meal. Bear this in mind as you add the liquid, as too much will dilute not only the flavour but also the nutritional value and substance. The bone stock used in meat stews will increase the nutritional value as well as flavour, so they may be a little thinner than the veggie versions.

When using meat, I like to cut it small, so that I get a mix of texture and flavour on my spoon or fork.

Chicken and rabbit can be easier to cook in portions, with the bones, which are removed once the meat is cooked.

Chefs will probably throw up their hands in horror, but I don't bother browning meat in batches – I simply stir it into the onion mix and once it's lost its red colour I add the flavourings then the stock. It seems to work fine – this is, after all, pragmatic home cooking.

Slow cookers can be very useful – if you assemble the ingredients in the morning it can be gently cooking all day, ready for your evening meal. You can also make your bone stock in a slow cooker.

Please play around. If you haven't got an ingredient, that's fine, just use a nutritionally equivalent substitute (eg a different herb, a different protein, different veg, etc) so that you're getting a similar nutrient profile.

Taste, taste and taste again, adjusting seasoning accordingly, while bearing in mind that we want to move away from sweetening food towards more savoury flavours.

Finally, although quantities are given, stews are very forgiving – don't get bogged down with weights.

MAKING A BONE STOCK/BROTH

● Get some bones from any meat from your butcher – these are often free, and if not, will be very cheap. Some will even come with a decent amount of meat on them. Don't trim anything off – all the bits we don't usually include will contribute to the nutritious content of your stock.

● Put the bones in a large saucepan and cover with cold water, add a few bay leaves and/or sprigs of thyme, a few peppercorns, pinch of salt and a cut up onion (include the onion skin for colour).

● Bring to the boil, then turn the heat as low as it will go and put the lid on.

● Leave to cook for at least 2 hours, preferably more (this is where a slow cooker can be really useful – I leave mine for 24 hours or more). Remember to keep checking the liquid level if it is on the stove top.

● Strain the liquid and add to soups and stews, or season it and drink it as it is.

You'll find other, slightly more involved recipes, but this seems to work well. Some people put some lemon juice or cider vinegar in the water to help extract more minerals from the bones. I'm afraid I usually forget.

VEGETABLE STOCK

You can make a tasty liquid for your veggie version by putting a mixture of root vegetables, onions and herbs into a pan of water with some seasoning, and cook gently for an hour with the lid on. Do use any vegetable trimmings and peelings as well, and consider adding some ginger, turmeric and/or seaweed, but pick your flavourings to fit with the flavours of your stew.

BASIC STEW

I use a similar base for all my stews, so this follows, with variations and suggestions for flavours. Meat stews have pulses added, which bumps up the nutritional value, making it economical AND healthy.

Bear in mind that meat stocks add a depth of flavour which is more of a challenge with vegan stews and vegetable stocks, so do check the seasoning and add more herbs, spices etc. Miso and tamarind can be useful taste boosters in both meat and vegetarian stews.

Per person, use:

- 1 onion, chopped or sliced

- 1 small-medium leek, sliced, including the green bits

- 1 carrot or equivalent sized piece of sweet potato, root veg or squash

- Any other vegetables you would like to use (no rules, except greens should be added at the end, as long-cooked greens can taste too bitter)

Fry this gently in olive oil until everything is slightly softened.

Add herbs and seasoning (bouillon powder is great for this).

Add meat, fish and/or pre-cooked pulses* at this stage and top up with your home-made stock. Don't worry about sealing the meat and cooking in small batches; this is pragmatic home cooking, and it works.

Cover and cook 1-2 hours for meat, 20-30 minutes for fish and pulses.

Taste and check the seasoning.

I cook the pulses separately in unsalted water because I've found that cooking with seasoning takes longer and sometimes results in harder beans. This is especially the case with salt and tomatoes. For more information on cooking pulses, see page 7.

The following Tina's Kitchen favourites serve 4-6 people generously. There is a meat and veggie version of most of them, and I've suggested what kind of meat to use in brackets. Please don't be put off if you are veggie and there's a meat in the title; simply use more pulses and a vegetable stock.

MOROCCAN STYLE STEW
(LAMB, CHICKEN, RABBIT)

For a vegan version double the pulses and use stock or water. The meat version can be made with any meat plus the pulses.

- Olive oil, meat fat or butter for frying

- 3 onions, chopped or sliced

- 2-3 small-medium leeks, sliced, including the green bits

- 2 carrots or equivalent sized piece of sweet potato or squash, cut into cubes

- 1-4 cloves of garlic, crushed or chopped

- 2-4 tbsp of grated fresh ginger

- 2 tsp each: cinnamon, ground cumin, ground coriander, paprika

- 1-2 tsp stock powder or cube or salt to taste

- 500g meat (lamb, chicken and rabbit all work well)

- ½ to ¾ litre stock or water

- 500g cooked pulses (double if making a veggie version) – eg cannellini beans, black-eyed-beans, lentils

- 1 medium apple, sliced/diced or half a finely sliced lemon/orange, including the peel

- 50-100g chopped dried fruit – dates, apricots or sultanas

- 2 tbsps fresh herbs – coriander, parsley or dill

Fry the onions, leeks and carrots gently in olive oil until everything is soft.

When the onions are translucent, add the garlic, ginger, spices and stock powder/salt. Add the meat, cut into cubes, and stir until light brown.

Add the stock, fruit and cooked pulses, stir and bring to the boil, then reduce to a simmer, cover and cook for 1-2 hours depending on the meat used. Stir occasionally. The veggie version will only need 20-30 minutes.

When the meat is cooked, taste the mixture and adjust the seasoning to your taste.

Add the fresh chopped herbs just before serving.

The whole lemon dressing on page 26 works like preserved lemons, so can be served alongside.

Optional extras:

- Peppers
- Celery
- Greens (at the end)
- Chilli
- Olives

LENTIL, ORANGE & ANISEED STEW
(GAME, RABBIT, CHICKEN, LAMB)

For a vegan version, omit the meat, double the pulses and use a home-made vegetable stock.

- Olive oil, meat fat or butter for frying

- 3 onions, chopped or sliced

- 2-3 leeks depending on size, sliced, including the green bits

- 1 medium sized beetroot, scrubbed and cut into very small dice

- 1 medium sweet potato or a couple of carrots, cut into dice

- 2 dsp finely grated fresh ginger

- 1-2 whole star anise

- 1 orange with peel, Seville if available, cut into 8 segments then finely sliced; marmalade will also do (2 tbsps)

- 1-2 tsp stock powder or ½ - 1 tsp salt

- 500g venison or game mix, diced

- 500g cooked brown or green lentils (double for the veggie version)

- ½ - ¾ litre stock or water (chicken, beef or lamb stock all work)

- Salt and pepper to taste

Fry onions and leeks gently in olive oil or fat until soft.

Stir in the ginger, star anise and stock powder then add the beetroot, sweet potato/carrot and finely sliced orange (see page 7).

Add the diced meat and stir until light brown.

Add the stock or water and cooked lentils, bring to the boil, then reduce the heat, cover and cook for 1-2 hours (20-30 minutes if making without meat). Season to taste.

CHILLI (BEEF OR LAMB & CHICKEN LIVER)

I add organic chicken livers to the meat version because it is a fantastic multi-nutrient and many of us don't eat liver these days. If you chop it nice and small, it won't be noticed by those who feel they don't like liver.

Note that chilli and paprika belong to the nightshade family so if you are avoiding these, add heat with ginger and black pepper.

- Olive oil, meat fat or butter for frying

- 3 onions, sliced or chopped

- 3-5 cloves garlic, finely chopped or crushed

- 2-3 leeks depending on size, sliced, including the green bits

- 500g good quality, grass fed beef or lamb mince

- 200g organic chicken livers, cut into very small pieces (this is easier if it's semi defrosted)

- 1-2 tsp bouillon powder or ½ - 1 tsp salt

- 1 tsp dried oregano

- ½ - 1 tsp chilli powder or flakes OR 2-3 tsp dried ginger (1-2 tbsp grated fresh ginger)

- 1-2 tsp paprika (optional)

- ½ litre beef stock or water

- 2 tins red kidney beans, pinto beans, black beans or similar (or about 500g cooked beans) – you could even use baked beans

- Salt and pepper to taste

Fry onions, leeks and garlic gently in olive oil or fat until soft.

Add the mince and chicken livers, stir to break up and cook until no longer red.

Add the bouillon/salt, oregano, chilli/ginger and paprika and stir to mix.

Add the stock or water, followed by the beans, and bring to the boil.

Cover and cook for 30-45 minutes, then taste and adjust the seasoning.

Variations

● If you like tomato with your chilli, but would prefer less nightshades, try adding a mixture of 100g grated beetroot and 100g butternut squash or sweet potato – it gives the right colour and imitates the flavour of tomatoes brilliantly.

● Add greens at the end – kale is robust enough, and spinach wilts very quickly.

● Add carrot or other vegetables to the stew to make it a more complete meal – less authentic but it adds to the nutrient value.

● **Try adding a mixture of lime juice and fresh coriander at the end.**

MUSHROOM, SWEET POTATO AND LENTIL/MUNG BEAN STEW

Mushroom and lentil or mung bean stew is very popular at Tina's Kitchen. The trick to getting a rich mushroom flavour is to cook the mushrooms in the oven first, and in this version all the vegetables get cooked in this way, making it a very simple stew. It will work well without mushrooms, if mushrooms are not your thing. You are aiming for a nice, thick and creamy consistency, and I like it nice and peppery.

Heat the oven to 180°C/350°F/Gas 4

You need a large baking tray, big enough to spread all the vegetables on – use two if necessary.

● 500g mushrooms, cut into slices

● 2-3 onions, sliced (red onions give a lovely flavour)

● 2-3 leeks, sliced (use the green bits, too)

● 2 medium sweet potatoes, no need to peel, just scrub and cut into cubes

- Olive oil

- 1 tsp salt

- 1 tsp black pepper

- 1 tsp dried thyme (or fresh)

- Cooked brown/green lentils or mung beans (500g cooked weight or 2 drained tins)

- Water or stock

- Salt and pepper to taste

- Chopped spinach or kale

Put the mushrooms, leeks, sweet potatoes, onions, thyme, salt and pepper on the baking tray/s, mix with enough olive oil to coat everything, and bake in the oven for 30-40 minutes, until the mushrooms have taken on a rich, dark colour.

Meanwhile you can be cooking your lentils or mung beans in a pot big enough to take the vegetables as well. They will also take around 30-40 minutes.

Tip the mushroom mixture into your lentils or mung beans and top up with stock or water if necessary. Remember, you want a thick and creamy consistency, so don't add too much liquid.

Stir, bring to the boil, taste and adjust the seasoning.

Add some finely chopped spinach or kale at the very end.

Variations

- Add some ground hazelnuts for extra protein, B vitamins and minerals

- Make with a chicken stock for extra nutrition and flavour

- This stew makes a great base for the Layered Bean Bake on page 61

RED LENTIL OR MUNG BEAN DAL

- 200g dried red lentils or mung beans, soaked

- 1 block creamed coconut - cut off the clearer oil part for frying the onions, chop the rest and set aside

- 2-3 onions, sliced or chopped

- 2-3 leeks, sliced, including the green parts

- 2-3 cloves garlic, chopped or crushed

- 1 tsp fresh turmeric, finely grated, or 1 tsp dried

- 1 dsp fresh ginger, finely grated, or 2 tsp dried

- 2-4 tsp curry powder (I make a simple one with equal quantities of ground cumin, coriander and fenugreek)

- 1-2 tsp bouillon powder or ½ - 1 tsp salt, start with a smaller amount and adjust as necessary.

- Black pepper

Boil the lentils/beans then reduce heat and simmer to cook for around 30-40 minutes until soft and mushy.

Meanwhile, melt the oil from the creamed coconut in a saucepan, add the onions, leeks and garlic, and gently fry until translucent.

Add the grated ginger and turmeric, stir to mix, then add the bouillon/salt and curry powder.

Tip in the cooked lentils/beans with their liquid and add some more water if necessary – you want it quite thick, like a Greek yogurt.

Add the chopped creamed coconut and cook gently until completely melted. Chopping it into little pieces first means it will melt more quickly and evenly.

Add pepper, taste and adjust the seasoning.

Additions

- Finely chopped spinach, kale or other green vegetables at the last minute

- Chopped fresh coriander or parsley

- Sprinkle mixed seeds over the top (not very Indian but it works, and adds extra nutritional value)

CURRIED FISH STEW

This is a favourite – it was the original stew I made for the Friday market with local fish. It is the only stew without pulses, but we have served it as a 'half and half' with the lentil dal, which works well.

- 1 block creamed coconut - cut off the clearer oil part for frying onions, chop the rest quite small, and set aside

- 2-3 onions, sliced or chopped

- 2-3 leeks, sliced, including the green parts

- 2-3 cloves garlic, chopped or crushed

- 1 tsp fresh turmeric, finely grated, or 1 tsp dried

- 1 dsp fresh ginger, finely grated, or 2 tsp dried

- 2-4 tsp curry powder (I make a simple one with ground cumin, coriander, fenugreek)

- 1-2 tsp bouillon powder or ½ -1 tsp salt to taste

- 500g fish pie mix or whatever fish you have available

- 1 litre fish stock or water

Melt the oil from the creamed coconut in a saucepan, add the onions, leeks and garlic, and gently fry until translucent.

Add the grated ginger and turmeric, stir to mix, then add the bouillon/salt and curry powder.

Add the stock or water and bring to the boil, then reduce to a simmer.

Add the chopped creamed coconut, stir and cook gently until completely melted. Chopping it into little pieces first means it will melt more quickly and evenly.

Add the fish and cook for 15-20 minutes until cooked, stirring occasionally. Don't worry if the fish breaks up, it still tastes great.

Taste and adjust the seasoning.

Additions

● Finely chopped spinach, kale or other green vegetables at the last minute.

● Chopped fresh coriander or parsley.

Variations

● **Thai style fish stew** – make as above, but instead of curry powder use Thai green curry paste (or red).

● **Fish Pie** – use steamed sweet potatoes as a topping for either of these mixes. Mash it with butter or olive oil and a little salt and pepper and bake in the oven until the sweet potato is slightly crispy on top, about 45 minutes.

CURRIED LENTIL/MUNG BEAN STEW (LAMB)

Apologies for the long ingredient list. Assemble the spices first and it will all feel much easier. If you are short of some of the spices, don't worry – just make it with what you've got; it will work even if you've only got a couple of things. Taste it near the end to decide how much salt and pepper to add, remembering that black pepper helps the absorption of many nutrients, including those of turmeric.

● Olive oil, butter, coconut oil or meat fat

● 2-3 onions, sliced or chopped

● 2-3 leeks, sliced, including the green parts

- 2 bay leaves

- Spices – assemble before you start: 2 cloves, 2 cardamom pods, ¼ tsp cayenne/chilli (optional), 1-2 tsp paprika, ½ cinnamon stick, 2 tsp ground coriander, 2 tsp ground cumin

- 2 dsp fresh ginger, 1 tsp fresh turmeric & 3-6 peeled garlic cloves, blended into a thick paste with water

- 500g diced lamb shoulder or braising steak

- ¾ litre home-made lamb/beef or vegetable stock

- 500g cooked whole lentils or mung beans (2 tins) (double if making the veggie version)

- Salt and pepper to taste

If you are cooking your own lentils or mung beans, put them in a pot with plenty of water and set them to boil, reducing them to a simmer for around 30 minutes.

Gently fry the onions and leeks in the oil or fat until translucent.

Add the meat if using, stir and cook until it has lost its red colour.

Add the dried spices and bay leaves and stir.

Stir in the ginger, turmeric and garlic paste.

Add the cooked lentils/mung beans with their cooking water or meat stock. You may need more liquid with the vegetarian version.

Stir, cover and cook gently until the meat is tender (1 ½ -2 hours) or until the flavours have blended if not using meat (around 30 mins).

Optional extras: fresh coriander, coconut cream/block, finely chopped greens

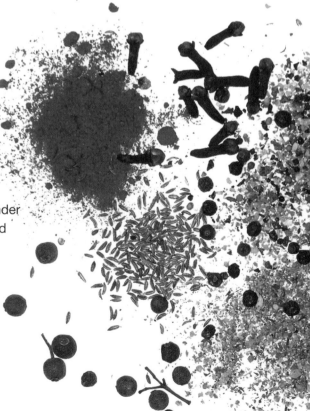

WHITE BEAN, ANISEED & GINGER STEW (PORK)

This is delicious – you can add some chopped dried apricots or leave it as it is. It does come out quite pale, but don't let that put you off – I find the addition of some chopped greens can make a big difference to the appearance. It will taste lovely whatever you do.

- Olive oil, butter or meat fat

- 2-3 onions, sliced or chopped

- 2-3 leeks, sliced, including the green parts

- 2-3 cloves garlic, chopped or crushed

- 500g diced pork shoulder

- 1 whole star anise

- 2 tbsp finely grated fresh ginger or 2 tsp powdered ginger

- 1-2 tsp bouillon powder or ½ - 1 tsp salt

- 2 tins white cannellini beans (or 200g dried and soaked for several hours) – double if making the veggie version

- ¾ litre home-made stock or water

- 50-100g chopped dried apricots or a finely cut up apple (optional)

- Salt and pepper to taste

If you are using dried beans, set them to boil – they can take up to 2 hours or more; it's a good idea to cook larger batches of beans and freeze them in portion sized bags/containers, then they can be used like tins of pre-cooked beans.

Fry onions, leeks and garlic gently in olive oil or fat until soft.

Add the meat and stir and cook until it is no longer red.

Add the ginger, star anise and bouillon, stir to mix and add the stock or water along with the cooked beans (or you can be cooking the beans separately at the same time, adding them to the stew once the meat is cooked).

Bring to the boil, add apricots if using, then reduce the heat, cover and cook gently for a couple of hours or 30 minutes if making the veggie version.

Note, although both beans and meat are cooked for a couple of hours, don't cook the raw soaked beans with the meat – the salt and flavourings can slow down the cooking and sometimes prevent the beans from softening up.

You can add chilli or more ginger and black pepper for a hotter taste.

Variations

- Swap the pork for beef and add a few finely chopped prunes instead of apricots.

- Try different beans.

BEANY STEW

This comes out a bit like home made baked beans, but instead of using tomatoes, the recipe uses squash or sweet potato along with beetroot; this gives a lovely tomatoey colour and tastes a bit like tomato, too, without the potential inflammatory issues associated with the nightshade family.

- Olive oil

- 2-3 onions, sliced or chopped

- 2-3 leeks, sliced (use the green bits, too)

- 1 medium grated beetroot (no need to peel)

- About a handful of peeled butternut squash or medium sweet potato, cut into small pieces

- 1 tsp salt

- 1 tsp black pepper

- 1 tsp dried thyme, oregano or other herbs, fresh or dried

- 500g cooked black-eyed beans (see* for alternatives)

- Water or stock

Heat olive oil in a large saucepan and add the onions and leeks.

Stir occasionally and cook until soft.

Add the beetroot and squash, stir then add the bouillon, herbs and pepper.

Stir in the cooked beans and bring to a boil, adding more water if necessary.

Cover and allow to simmer gently until everything is cooked through, about 20-30 minutes.

Taste and adjust the seasoning.

You can use any beans here – pinto beans, cannellini, kidney beans or butter beans would work well, so use whatever you have.

PEA & MINT STEW (HAM)

- Olive oil
- 1-2 bay leaves
- 2-3 onions, sliced or chopped
- 2-3 leeks, sliced (use the green bits, too)
- 500g ham hock, soaked and boiled for a couple of hours (keep the liquid)
- 500g dried green peas, soaked overnight, or a bag of frozen peas
- 1 tsp dried sage and a tablespoon of chopped fresh mint or 1-2 tsp mint sauce
- Salt & pepper to taste

If cooking your own peas, set them to boil for around an hour, until soft and mushy. Don't be tempted to cook them with the ham, as its saltiness may prevent the peas cooking properly.

Remove the ham from the bone once cooked, and chop into pieces.

Gently fry the onions, leeks and bay leaves in the olive oil until translucent.

Add the sage, ham and peas, stir and bring back to the boil with the ham cooking liquid or water.

Taste and add salt (IF NEEDED) and pepper along with the mint.

LENTIL/BEAN, LEMON & THYME STEW (CHICKEN)

- Olive oil

- 2-3 onions, sliced or chopped

- 2-3 leeks, sliced (use the green bits, too)

- 2-4 cloves of garlic, crushed or chopped

- 1-2 bay leaves

- Other vegetables – carrots, sweet potato, parsnip, for example

- 500g chicken – cooked or raw

- 500g cooked lentils or beans of any kind (double for the veggie version)

- 1 whole organic lemon (you will use the peel as well)

- ½ - 1 tsp dried thyme or a few fresh sprigs

- ¾ litre chicken or vegetable stock

- Salt & pepper to taste

Gently fry the onions and leeks with the garlic and bay leaves until translucent.
Add any other vegetables, cut into small pieces, and stir into the onion mix along with the thyme.

Cut the chicken into bite sized pieces if using, put into the pan and stir, then add the lentils/beans and stock. You can also use chicken pieces and remove the bones once the meat is cooked.

Cut the lemon into tiny pieces (into segments first, then slice finely into little fan shapes, page 7) and add to the stew, then simmer until the chicken is cooked through – about 30-40 minutes.

Taste and adjust the seasoning.

BLACK BEAN, LIME, TURMERIC & GINGER STEW (BEEF)

- Olive oil, butter or meat fat

- 2-3 onions, sliced or chopped

- 2-3 leeks, sliced, including the green parts

- 2-3 cloves garlic, chopped or crushed

- 500g beef shin or other stewing beef, cut into cubes

- 2 tbsp finely grated fresh ginger

- 1 tbsp finely grated fresh turmeric or 1 tsp dried

- 1-2 tsp bouillon powder

- 2 tins black beans (or 200g dried and soaked for several hours) – double for veggie version

- ¾ litre stock or water

- 1-2 limes

If you are using dried beans, set them to boil – they can take up to 2 hours or more; it's a good idea to cook larger batches of beans and freeze them in portion sized bags, then they can be used like tins of pre-cooked beans.

Fry onions, leeks and garlic gently in olive oil or fat until soft.

Add the meat and stir and cook until it is no longer red.

If the lime skins are soft, either cut them very finely (into segments then tiny fan shapes) or blitz them in a blender. If the skin is hard, cut it off and chop the flesh of the lime, then add to the stew.

Add the ginger, turmeric and bouillon, stir to mix and add the stock or water along with the cooked beans (or you can be cooking the beans separately at the same time, adding them to the stew once the meat is cooked).

Bring to the boil, reduce the heat and cook gently for a couple of hours, (20-30 minutes for the veggie version), stirring occasionally.

Note: although both beans and meat are cooked for a couple of hours, don't cook the raw soaked beans with the meat – the salt and flavourings can slow down the cooking and sometimes prevent the beans from softening up.

You can add chilli or more ginger and black pepper for a hotter taste.

LAYERED BEAN BAKE

Layered bean bake is a lasagne-inspired bake, using cashew sauce instead of white sauce, and layers of vegetables instead of lasagne. This makes it lower carbohydrate, higher protein and more nutrient dense, which could help balance blood sugar levels and support weight management and mood.

Use any of the stews for the bean part of the bake – veggie or meat.

You need a rectangular oven dish (something like a lasagne dish) – no need to grease it.

As well as your stew base, you need:

● 500g cashew nuts with soaking water plus another 300ml

● 1 onion

● Bouillon powder or salt

● Some vegetables to make the layers – spinach, kale, opened leeks, mushrooms, very thin slices of squash or sweet potato

● ● ●

Make the Cashew Sauce

Soak the cashew nuts in water for 2-3 hours. I have made it with just a few minutes' soaking, and it works fine. You just get a creamier sauce if you soak for longer.

Drain and discard the water.

Peel and cut the onion into chunks.

Mix the cashew nuts, onion, 1 tsp bouillon powder and 300ml of water in a bowl. You need 60ml of water per 100g of cashew nuts.

Liquidise in batches, depending on the size of your mixer.

Taste and add more bouillon if you think it needs it.

You need the sauce to be quite thick and smooth.

Slice some vegetables very finely to use as layers.

Try to use something different from what's in your stew so that you have more variety in your meal.

Heat the oven to 180°C/350°F/Gas 4

Assemble the bake

This is just like a lasagne: put a layer of the stew in the bottom of your dish, lay vegetable slices on top then pour on a layer of sauce. Repeat until your dish is full, finishing with a layer of sauce. You'll probably get 2 or 3 layers, depending on the size of your dish.

Sprinkle some paprika (optional) on top and bake in the oven for 50-60 minutes.
It is ready when it's a nice golden colour and the sauce has set - it is almost sponge like.
Serve with another vegetable or salad – something different from what is in the bake.

'TOADS'

Toads are mini toad in the holes, and you can make a vegan/veggie version or a meat version. Don't stop there though – let your imagination create your own variations. Instead of a standard batter, use the cashew sauce on the previous page.

Use muffin tins, well oiled, or silicone moulds on a tray. Dollop about a dessertspoon of cashew sauce into each hole, then put your filling (a spoonful of stew, chopped mushrooms, cheese and ham or pieces of good quality sausage) into it.

Bake in the oven (180°C/350°F/Gas 4) for about 40-50 minutes until firm and golden brown. Allow to settle in the tins before removing and cooling on a rack or serving warm.

Cakey things

... and not-so-sweet treats

We all like a sweet treat, but our taste buds have become so used to sweet foods that many people find it difficult to enjoy the savoury and slightly bitter foods which are so good for us. For this reason I don't go overboard on the sweet stuff, while making it as nutrient dense as possible.

I've devised a few sweetish snacks and cakey things to tick the 'treat' box without causing blood sugar spikes. They contain good fats, protein in the form of nuts and eggs and are generally higher in fibre and lower in carbohydrate, all of which can help blood sugar balance.

The sweetness is provided with coconut, vanilla, cinnamon, whole dried fruit, oranges and in three cases the addition of maple syrup or honey in small quantities.

While maple syrup and honey can be viewed as healthier sweeteners, make no mistake, they are still sweet, and basically sugars.

The chocolate used is 73% dark organic chocolate, which will contain some ordinary sugar, but the higher the cocoa content, the lower the added sugar.

Sweet things, even without added sugar, need to be put in their proper place. They are a treat. The good thing about these treats is that they tend to satisfy the sweet craving/ desire instead of leaving you wanting more, unlike most sweet foods.

SWEET CASHEW CREAM

This is a great accompaniment for cakey things, fruit and other puddings. It adds a decent amount of protein to your meal and is dairy free.

Soak 100g cashew nuts for a couple of hours in water, drain, add 60-100ml fresh water or nut milk, 1 whole lime (peel cut off), half a teaspoon vanilla essence and whizz in a machine until smooth. Taste and adjust the flavour if necessary.

CARAWAY NUTS

- 1 dsp coconut oil

- 1.5 dsp honey or maple syrup

- ½-1 tsp sea salt

- 4 tsp caraway seeds

- 1 pinch chilli powder or flakes (optional)

- 300g mixed nuts and pumpkin seeds

You need a baking tray lined with parchment paper.

In a large pan, melt the coconut oil and honey and heat until gently bubbling.

Add the salt, caraway seeds and chilli. Stir, add the nuts and mix until everything is coated. Spread in a single layer onto a sheet of baking parchment or silicone until it has cooled. Break into pieces and store in an airtight jar.

SALTED CHOCOLATE NUTS

- 100g good quality, dark (70% or more) organic chocolate

- 1/3 tsp sea salt

- 120g mixed nuts of your choice

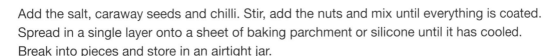

You need a baking tray lined with parchment paper.

Melt the chocolate in a bowl or jug over hot water.

Add the salt, mix well then stir in the nuts.

Spread in a single layer on a sheet of parchment paper or silicone and allow to cool, then break it up into pieces and store in an airtight jar.

CHOCOLATE ALMOND CRUNCH

This definitely ticks the chocolate box with no added sugar, and all the sweetness comes from whole dates, which are fibre rich and help slow down the release of sugar.

Halve the quantities for a smaller mixture, but it does keep for several weeks.

You will need a shallow baking tray lined with non-stick parchment paper, plus another sheet to lay on top. The full mixture is usually just under 1cm thick, but it can be any thickness you like.

- 240g cocoa butter

- 200g dates (without stones)

- 170g (1 jar) almond butter

- 130g cocoa/cacao powder

- 150g cacao nibs

- 1 tsp vanilla essence

- 1 tsp cinnamon

- ½ tsp salt

Melt the cocoa butter in a jug or bowl over hot water.

Meanwhile, finely chop the dates in a food processor, add everything except the cocoa butter and pulse until it is blended.

Pour the melted cocoa butter into the mixture with the motor running for a few seconds, until blended.

Scrape/pour the mixture into the parchment paper-lined tray. Lay another sheet of parchment paper on top and smooth the top with your hands. Leave to set.

When cool, cut into little squares and store in an airtight jar.

Note: Clean the food processor quickly, before the cocoa butter sets!

MOCK-CHOC

This came about because I (briefly) stopped caffeine and wanted a chocolate substitute which tasted good. It's made like Chocolate Almond Crunch. The full mixture is usually just under 1cm thick, but it can be any thickness you like.

Halve the quantities for a smaller mixture, but it does keep for several weeks.
You will need a shallow baking tray lined with non-stick parchment paper, plus another sheet to lay on top.

- 240g cocoa butter

- 250g soft prunes (no stones)

- 150g carob powder

- 1 jar hazelnut butter (170g)

- 2 tsp vanilla essence

- 1 tsp salt

Melt the cocoa butter over hot water.

Meanwhile, finely chop the prunes in a food processor, add everything except the cocoa butter and pulse until it is blended.

Pour the melted cocoa butter into the mixture with the motor running for a few seconds, until blended.

Scrape/pour the mixture into the parchment paper-lined tray. Lay another sheet of parchment paper on top and smooth the top with your hands. Leave to set.

Once set, cut into small squares and store in an airtight jar.

Note: Clean the food processor quickly, before the cocoa butter sets!

LIME & GINGER TAHINI BITES

These are a kind of 'energy ball', made with simple but delicious ingredients, and taste like a less sweet version of halva.

- 1 pack creamed coconut (200g) in its sealed plastic bag

- 3 tbsp tahini

- Zest of 2 limes, finely grated

- Thumb sized piece of ginger, finely grated (1.5 -2 tablespoons)

- 80g ground almonds

- 1 dsp maple syrup or honey

Boil the kettle, put the bag of coconut into a heatproof bowl and pour the boiling water over the top. Leave until it is completely pliable.

Mix everything else together in a bowl followed by the melted creamed coconut. Mix well and taste, adjusting the lime and ginger flavour as required. You need to do this fairly quickly before the coconut sets.

Roll into teaspoon sized balls and coat in sesame seeds or desiccated coconut and allow to set at room temperature. Alternatively, spread onto a parchment paper-lined tray, spread another sheet over the top and smooth it with your hands. When cool, cut into squares.

They are best kept in the fridge but will keep at room temperature for a week or so.

Try adding turmeric as well for extra benefits (anti-inflammatory, liver supportive and so much more).

SWEET POTATO CHOCOLATE CAKES

This is a great, not-too-sweet cake which will tick the chocolate, cake and pudding box without leaving you wanting more. It can be made dairy free with coconut oil, and if you leave the eggs out it becomes vegan – the texture is more dense but it still tastes great.

You will first cook the sweet potatoes, mash them, melt the chocolate, oil and maple syrup into the potato and finally add the dry ingredients and eggs.

Makes 12 in a silicone muffin tray.

- 400g sweet potatoes, peeled and cut into pieces
- 200g dark organic chocolate (70% or more)
- 12 extra squares or buttons of chocolate to finish (optional)
- 50g coconut oil or butter
- 60g maple syrup
- 2 eggs
- ½ tsp vanilla essence

Dry ingredients:

- 30g cocoa powder

- 100g ground almonds

- ½ tsp salt

- ½ tsp baking powder

- 1 tsp ground cinnamon

Steam the sweet potatoes until soft enough to mash (10-20 mins depending on the size of your pieces).

Meanwhile, put all the dry ingredients into a jug or bowl.

Heat the oven to 180°C/350°F/Gas 4

Drain the cooked potatoes, tip them back into the same pan and mash well.

While everything is still hot, put the chocolate and coconut oil/butter into the mashed sweet potato, mix until melted and then stir in the maple syrup and vanilla essence.

Add the dry ingredients and mix well, then add the eggs, mixing again until smooth.

Divide between 12 muffin moulds and smooth the tops with a spatula or palette knife. (If using silicone trays, put them onto baking sheets first) Cook for 20-25 mins until they separate slightly from the edge of the moulds.

When you take the cakes out of the oven, put a small square of dark chocolate on each one (optional). The heat of the cakes will melt the chocolate in a couple of minutes, then spread it with a palette knife.

Allow to cool in the trays and enjoy warm or cold with cream, yogurt, cashew cream, or just on its own.

They will keep for at least a week in the fridge and freeze well.

DATE & ALMOND CAKES Makes 12 cakes in a muffin mould.

Some people say this makes them think of Bakewell Tart; I made it because I used to love date slices, and now I think this is MUCH better. This might look like my most complicated recipe, but it's pretty straightforward really. It can be vegan, using coconut oil, or not, using butter.

First things first

Cut the peel off 1 medium orange then whizz the peel in a liquidiser or food processor and save for the next steps. Use the rest of the orange in the next step; there is no waste.

You will use the whole orange, split between filling and pastry. Now whizz the orange flesh separately and put to one side.

Pastry

- 250g ground almonds

- 100g desiccated coconut

- 125g salted butter or coconut oil for a dairy free and vegan version

- Whizzed flesh of 1 orange, without the peel (which goes with the dates)

- ½ tsp salt (1 tsp if using coconut oil)

Combine all the dry ingredients in a food processor until it resembles a crumble mix.

Add half the whizzed orange flesh, combine and then test by pinching a lump together – it should stick nicely without being too wet. Add more orange if necessary. Any leftover orange goes into the next step.

Date filling

- 250g soft pitted dates

- Zest of the orange, as above

- Any leftover orange flesh

Whizz it all up in a food processor or liquidiser and put to one side.

You can either assemble the cakes now or put the mixtures in the fridge for a while to make it easier to handle (not essential).

Heat the oven to 170°C/325°F/Gas 3

Assembly

Grease a muffin tin or use a silicone muffin tray resting on a baking sheet.

Divide the pastry mix in half, then each half into 12 equal sized balls or lumps (about a dessertspoon in size).

Divide the date mixture into 12 equal sized bits as well.

Lay a lump of pastry in the bottom of each muffin hole and press it gently to flatten.

Lay a flattened date lump on top of the pastry, then top each with another lump of pastry and smooth it over with the back of a spoon.

If you like, sprinkle some flaked almonds or desiccated coconut on the top and press lightly into the surface.

Bake in the oven for 10 minutes, then check; you may need to turn the tray round if your oven is uneven (as ours is). Bake for a further 10-15 minutes. They are ready when a light brown colour. If you have a hot oven, check sooner.

Allow them to cool in the muffin tray. They are quite fragile, and the longer they have to set, the easier they handle.

'Jaffa' Bites (Variation)

Mix together equal quantities of the date filling and pastry from the date cake recipe, roll it into little balls and flatten them (about the size of a 50p piece) onto a baking tray then bake like biscuits for around 15 minutes. Once out of the oven, while still hot, pop a small amount of dark chocolate on top, spreading it as it melts. They are delicious!

PRUNE & HAZELNUT BROWNIE

This is a delicious, rich chocolate brownie, using only prunes and orange for sweetness. You need a 20cm square tin, or a similar sized flan dish, well oiled, or lined with baking parchment.

- 150g dark organic chocolate (70% minimum)

- 100g butter or coconut oil

- 1 peeled orange

- 125g pitted dried or semi-dried prunes

- 2 eggs

Dry ingredients:

- 100g ground almonds

- 60g roughly chopped hazelnuts (keep a few aside for sprinkling on top)

- 20g cocoa powder

- 1 tsp baking powder

- 1 tsp vanilla essence

- ½ tsp salt

Melt the chocolate and butter/coconut oil gently in a bowl over a pan of hot water.

Heat the oven to 180°C/350°F/Gas 4

Whizz the orange and prunes together in a blender or food processor.

Add the melted chocolate, butter and orange prune mix to the dry ingredients then add the eggs.

Mix well and pour into your tin, smoothing the top. Sprinkle a few chopped hazelnuts on top.

Bake for 25 minutes. Allow to cool in the tin, then cut into squares.

Nutritional Nuggets

Oils, fats and other ingredients

● Always use **cold pressed olive oil**, not sunflower or other cheaper oils, as these are high in inflammatory Omega 6 fats, and are often damaged in their production. Extra virgin olive oil is an important part of the Mediterranean diet, high in antioxidants, and may help reduce inflammation.

● **Coconut oil** has been found to support healthy cholesterol balance.

● **Cold pressed flax or hemp oils** can be useful if you are vegetarian or vegan, as they contain some Omega 3 oils; be sure to buy them in dark, glass bottles and keep in the fridge once opened. Only use them cold, as heat damages them.

● **Raw cider vinegar** with the 'mother' may contain useful bacteria to support your gut. The acidity could also help digestion more generally.

● **Tamarind** has traditionally been used for all kinds of ailments including arthritis, constipation and poor digestion.

● **Unpasteurised miso** may support the gut with live bacteria.

● **Chocolate**, when dark (70% or more) and good quality (i.e. containing only cocoa, cocoa butter and relatively low sugar) is high in antioxidants and contains some magnesium and iron along with other minerals. Cocoa powder has the same benefits without the sugar.

● **Carob** is naturally sweet and caffeine free, so can be a useful alternative to chocolate if that's what you fancy.

Herbs and spices

Adding herbs and spices to your cooking helps bump up the beneficial properties of your food.

● **Aniseed, fennel, dill and caraway seeds** can help digestion and reduce flatulence.

● **Black pepper** contains piperine, which can help the body better absorb nutrients from the food you are eating.

● **Cinnamon** can make a food taste sweeter, and may help with blood sugar balancing.

● **Coriander** may help support detoxification and is a good source of potassium and vitamin K.

● **Garlic** can help support immunity and act as an antimicrobial and antifungal.

● **Ginger** has been shown to help reduce inflammation and is also useful for digestion.

● **Mustard** and other hot tastes can help the absorption of the magical anti-cancer properties of broccoli and other brassicas.

● **Parsley** is a magical ingredient. Even a small amount contains great levels of vitamins and minerals. It's a natural antimicrobial and aids the body's detoxification processes.

- **Thyme, rosemary and oregano** have antimicrobial and antifungal properties.

- **Turmeric** has been well studied for its anti-inflammatory, anti-cancer and liver supportive properties.

Meat and fish

- **Bone stock** extracts some of the nutritious minerals and collagen from bones, which may help with immunity and gut healing. The longer you cook it, the more you extract. While the body can't absorb collagen itself, digestion breaks it down and provides you with the building blocks to make your own. There is some thinking that because we usually avoid the skin and connective tissue in our cooking, we may be missing out on some essential nutrients for our own connective tissue; this may be a factor in bone, cartilage, tendon, skin and joint health. Using bone broths could help with this.

- **Wild meat** is as natural as you can get and is likely to have a healthy balance of fats, including useful amounts of Omega 3s.

- **Grass fed, free range beef** is likely to have a more natural balance of saturated and polyunsaturated fats, whereas intensively reared, inactive animals fed on unnatural foods are likely to be fatter overall and have less beneficial fats in their meat and produce.

- **Lamb** is probably one of the healthiest farmed meats, as it has to be grass fed and free range; this helps create a healthier fat profile.

- **Liver** is a nutrient dense food and eating it once every week or so provides a natural multi vitamin and mineral boost.

Some of things you'll get from eating good quality liver are: easily absorbable iron; B Vitamins; Selenium; CoQ10 – important for a healthy heart and energy production; Vitamin A – for immunity, skin and mucous membrane health; just 28g (1 oz) of liver gives 75% of our daily Vitamin A requirement. It also includes a recently identified 'anti-fatigue' factor. Including small amounts regularly in recipes with lots of other ingredients might be easier if you're not so keen on the taste.

Note: The NHS does not recommend consumption of liver in pregnancy.

- **Fish** is a healthy source of protein with a good balance of fats, minerals and vitamins including iodine, selenium and zinc – all of which are important for many functions in the body. Fish is used as part of an anti-inflammatory diet; inflammation is recognised as a contributory factor in many of our modern diseases, so eating fish regularly along with plenty of different vegetables, herbs and spices could help lower inflammation.

- **Oily fish** (sardines, mackerel, anchovies and salmon) contain good levels of Omega 3 oils, important for brain development and function, mental health and reducing inflammation.

Vegetables

- Aiming for a wide variety of plant foods is arguably more valuable than the idea of 5, 7 or 9 a day because different foods have different nutritional and medicinal properties, so the wider the variety, the more benefits you'll get. A simple trick is to aim for a 'rainbow' each day – pick veg and fruit of different colours. Adding green vegetables, onions and herbs, as well as other vegetables, helps increase your intake of important nutrients, so find a way of adding that little bit extra, every time you make something.

- Wherever possible, include **vegetable peel**, as it contains valuable fibre and nutrients.

- **Vegetable stocks** can be ready in an hour. They can contain good levels of potassium, and using herbs and spices can infuse them with some extra benefits.

- **Beetroot** is a wonderful food with many nutritional benefits, high in antioxidants, fibre and minerals and can support healthy blood pressure.

- **Bitter** leaves are said to stimulate digestive juices, so eating them on a regular basis could help improve digestion. Another benefit of bitter tastes is their ability to help retrain your taste buds. Taste can change within as little as a week, so even if you think something is too bitter for you, gradually introducing these kinds of foods will soon change how you experience them.

- **Courgettes** have good levels of fibre, Vitamins A and C, minerals and antioxidants. They are also a very low carb vegetable.

- **Brassicas** of all kinds are great 'superfoods'. Broccoli is the best known, but the family includes all cabbage, Brussels sprouts, watercress, pak choi, turnips and more. The term superfood can encourage us to leave out other foods, when what we are aiming for is variety. Use as many different varieties of this family, and other vegetable families, as possible during a week. The brassica family contains lots of nutrients helpful for detoxification, bowel health, reducing cancer risk and much more. Just eat them regularly.

- The humble **cabbage** is as wonderful as broccoli, so please do vary your brassicas. It is a great source of Vitamin C, choline (good for liver and brain), glutamine (for gut health and anti-inflammatory properties), B vitamins, Vitamin K and minerals.

- **Celery** is a bit of a star, containing many vitamins and minerals, good levels of fibre, antioxidants and anti-inflammatory compounds. It may be useful for cholesterol balance and immune support, as well as a digestive aid.

- **Mushrooms** of all kinds are thought to be immune supportive. Using more unusual varieties such as shitake can give you even more of these properties. Putting mushrooms upside down on a sunny windowsill for a couple of hours can help boost their Vitamin D content.

- **Onions, leeks and garlic** have many properties including supporting immune function and feeding your good bacteria.

- **Root vegetables** come in wonderful colours and are a good way to contribute to your rainbow each day. Ensuring a variety of colours from vegetables is a simple way of making sure you get a wide range of nutrients – vitamins, minerals and antioxidants. Root veg are a good source of fibre, which supports bowel and colon health as well as healthy cholesterol and hormone balance. They are also great for feeding the good bacteria which are now widely acknowledged to be essential for health and wellbeing, both physical and mental. Root vegetables are higher in carbohydrate than the green leafy stuff, but it is a great, complex carbohydrate which is slow to convert into sugars. They can help to make a meal feel more filling without resorting to more nutrient light carbs.

- **Sprouted seeds** are a source of concentrated nutrition. You can grow sprouts from many different seeds and beans; try lentils, sunflower seeds and pumpkin seeds. I've found you can just use organic seeds from your store cupboard rather than buying special sprouting seeds, so do experiment. Radish sprouts have a hot taste, which has been shown to increase the absorption of the good stuff from the brassica vegetables. Unfortunately they aren't so easy to get hold of unless you grow your own, but good old mustard cress from the supermarket will work too. Broccoli sprouts are super-super foods, containing very high concentrations of magical cancer-fighting nutrients including sulforaphane.

- **Sweet potatoes** are high in fibre, B vitamins, beta carotene and antioxidants.

Fruits

- **Apples** are full of all sorts of goodies including vitamin C, pectin (which helps with bowel function) and fibre, which among other things has been found to help balance cholesterol.

- **Whole dates** are naturally sweet, contain fibre and a whole range of vitamins and minerals, so are nutritionally far superior to sugar or sugar substitutes. If you are tempted to use date syrup instead of whole dates, do remember that this is just the sugar extracted from the fruit without the benefit of the fibre to slow down its release. Whole food is always going to be superior to any extract.

- Using **whole lemons** and other citrus means that you are including important antioxidants like limonene and naringen. It also adds a slightly bitter taste, which has a couple of benefits: it can help retrain our taste buds to expect less sweet foods and it may help stimulate digestive juices, enzymes and bile, which in turn improves our digestion.

- **Pomegranates** are magical fruits, making your food look beautiful and taste delicious as well as providing valuable antioxidants which may help reduce inflammation, reduce cancer risk and support blood sugar balancing. They even have anti-fungal and anti-bacterial properties. So it's well worth the effort – prepare a whole pomegranate at a time and store the seeds in the fridge in a glass jar, so you can sprinkle a tablespoon or so onto your food. Do enjoy the process of gently teasing out the jewel-like seeds – it can be quite meditative.

- We all know **oranges** are a good source of vitamin C, but did you know that it is also in the peel?

- **Prunes** add useful fibre as well as vitamins and minerals and are considered good for bone health. They also have a slight sharpness alongside their sweet taste, which might help retrain our taste buds.

Pulses

- The addition of pulses to any dish provides an added layer of nutrition – fibre, B vitamins, minerals and complex carbohydrate, helping cholesterol balance, the health of the gut bacteria and blood sugar balance. Pulses contain less protein than animal sources, so vegetarians need to add nuts, seeds or eggs to top up the protein and get a wider range of amino acids.

Nuts and seeds

- Nuts and seeds provide good levels of protein, fibre, B vitamins, magnesium, zinc and other minerals.

- Using ground nuts used instead of flour in baking reduces the carbs, increases the protein and nutrient density, and can help with blood sugar balance.

- Using cashew sauce adds more nutritional value in the form of protein, good fats, minerals and vitamins.

- **Tahini** is a useful source of protein, magnesium, calcium, zinc and B Vitamins.

- Although cooking seeds can reduce some of their nutritional value, eating them in any form is better for you than none at all; not all nutrients will be affected by cooking.

Eggs

- Eggs are a fantastic food: good quality protein, satisfying and containing all necessary nutrients except Vitamin C. They are also a source of choline, which is essential for brain development and mental health. Eggs, when served with salad, help the absorption of the nutrients from your salad – a match made in heaven!

Salt

- Good quality sea salt contains a range of useful minerals, and because it is so much more flavoursome you need less than table salt, which is lower in nutrients.

Nutrition in a nutshell...

While this is primarily a recipe book, I want to emphasise the idea that food is there to nourish us, not simply refuel us - every ingredient should have a purpose. If you're interested to know more about the thinking behind these recipes, here are my basic guidelines, with explanations to follow:

● Make every mouthful count (maximise nutrient density)

● Include protein with every meal and snack (meat, fish, eggs, pulses, nuts, seeds, cheese)

● Concentrate on complex carbohydrates like vegetables, pulses, nuts and seeds while keeping simple carbohydrates (the obvious carbs like sugar, bread, pasta, rice etc.) to a minimum

● Use only good quality fats (olive oil, butter, coconut oil, fat from naturally reared animals)

● Aim for a rainbow of natural colours in vegetables and fruits each day

● Maximise your plant intake, including herbs, spices, vegetables, fruit, pulses, nuts, seeds etc – whether you're veggie or not

● Variety in everything – the more variety you have, the more nutrients you'll be taking in

The aim of this is to:

● Balance blood sugar levels, which can affect energy, mood, hormones and weight along with cholesterol balance, heart health and brain health.

● Provide maximum nutrient density – ticking lots of nutritional boxes to enable our bodies to function well.

● Provide nutrients to help us deal with stress, toxins and inflammation.

The value of food – treat yourself to better health

Our cells are constantly replacing, and they can only be built out of what we put into our bodies - we really are what we eat. With the right ingredients we get a well put-together, efficient body. If some are missing or poor quality, it'll be clunky, inefficient and go wrong. We need a multitude of nutrients to replace these cells, help them do their jobs and to make lots of different processes in the body run smoothly. Provide these nutrients by eating a varied diet.

Think of the three little pigs – we build a straw house when we eat nutrient poor food, and a nice strong brick house when we eat nutrient dense, varied real food. (This image comes from Tom O'Bryan in The Autoimmune Fix)

Our spending on food is now a fraction of what it used to be. Eating healthily is thought to be expensive, but we need to move away from the idea that food is effortless and cheap, towards the understanding that it is essential to health and wellbeing, therefore essential to society and the economy. We also need to rediscover the pleasure of creating nourishing food for ourselves and our families.

In my opinion, food is the ONLY thing worth spending money and time on (along with shoes – remaining mobile and on our feet greatly affects quality of life, especially as we get older). Consider the cost of those little extra 'treats' we all indulge in to make up for the stressful, tiring lives we lead: coffee, alcohol, snacks, chocolate, meals out, cigarettes, beauty products and treatments. Even one coffee a day at around £2.50 adds up to £15 a week – enough for an organic veg box.

Once we start to feed ourselves well – truly nourish our bodies – these things find their proper place as occasional indulgences. We might find our skin, hair and nails look better, saving money on beauty products. Maybe there are less headaches and digestive issues, saving money on over the counter remedies. We might even take less days off sick, making work more efficient and time off more of a pleasure.

Your health dictates your quality of life and therefore your happiness, energy, effectiveness, relationships, wellbeing and more. If you invest in your health by buying good food and cooking from scratch, the benefits you reap are priceless.

The rise of nutrient-light processed 'food' is something we also need to recognise. Much of what is sold as food does not feed us – there is little or no nourishment in it, and the more processed it is (i.e. the more changes which have been made to the original ingredients) the higher the demands placed on our bodies to detoxify additives and extract what little nutrition it contains.

In an ideal world we would get all our nutrients from food, but:

● Much of what is available cannot be defined as nourishing food which should be fuelling our bodies and building healthy cells.

● Farming and production methods mean that the nutrient content of many foods has declined over the last 100 years.

● We have massive demands on our detoxification processes because of the 'new to nature' chemicals which are constantly being introduced.

● We have 24/7 lives where we never feel we have done enough, are constantly comparing ourselves to others and feel under enormous pressures from all directions.

So while we place more demands on our bodies, we have fewer resources to help us deal with them – not only are we eating a lot of non-food, but even the real food is lower in nutritional value than it used to be.

We help address this challenge by eating nutrient dense food, supporting our bodies to function well and helping us deal with stress. It has probably never been more important for us to focus on nutrient dense real food and put the non-foods firmly in their place – they do not feed us, so I would say they shouldn't even be called food.

I want to challenge the idea of a treat – by indulging in non-nutritious food and drink we are requiring more from our bodies to process them while providing less tools to do it with. We are treating our bodies unkindly. To treat them kindly, eat good, natural food, most of the time. Enjoy occasional indulgences, recognise them for what they are and don't beat yourself up about them.

Nutritional equivalence

I've recently come up with the idea of nutritional equivalence. When people stop eating meat, fish and animal products, they may simply eat more vegetables, which are not the same thing, nutritionally. Eating more veg is great for all of us, of course, but we still need amino acids (from proteins), minerals and vitamins, many of which are more plentiful in animal products. So if we decide to give up animal products we need to substitute foods which tick the same nutritional boxes – foods which are nutritionally equivalent.

For example, when swapping dairy milk for soya or nut milk, which has lower protein and synthetic vitamins, we are not swapping like for like, nutritionally. Similarly, vegan cheeses are often made simply to imitate taste and texture, not nutritional value. Look for those made with 'real' ingredients containing a decent amount of protein; cheese has around 25g of protein per 100g, plus vitamins and minerals, so you're looking for something similar in a cheese replacement. Vegan cheeses I have seen (apart from one made from cashew nuts) tend to contain only 1-2g of protein per 100g. If you use something with a lesser nutritional profile, find something to fill the gaps – look for your protein elsewhere.

When using these recipes, if you don't fancy including a suggested ingredient, substitute it for something which has a similar nutritional value – a protein for a different protein, a vegetable for a different vegetable and a herb or spice for a different herb or spice, so that the dish is still serving a similar nutritional purpose.

Make every mouthful count – the most important rule!

Food should be nourishing us by ticking lots of nutritional boxes – amino acids, fats, vitamins, minerals, antioxidants, fibre and so on. Given the demands on our bodies in the modern world and the abundance of empty calories (food and drink with no nutritional benefits), it's important to make every mouthful count; thinking this way can be a great help when it comes to deciding what to eat and what not to eat.

As an illustration, imagine you are hungry between meals, and have a choice of a small packet of almonds or low-fat crisps. The calories are roughly the same, so which will you choose if you are trying to lose weight? You may have picked up the idea that nuts are fattening and therefore the crisps are a better option because they are lower in fat, but when you compare the nutrient content you might think differently.

● Nuts have protein, good fats, minerals and vitamins in them, while crisps have pure carbohydrate, cheap salt and unhealthy fats.

● Nuts will help you feel fuller for longer, whereas there's a fair chance a packet of crisps will leave you hungry after a short time and wanting to eat more. At the same time the unhealthy fats and sugars in the crisps make more demands on the body.

In the long run, then, the crisps lead you to eat more calories with less nutrition!

When you are making food choices, try to weigh up the nutritional content:

● How processed is it - how different from the original ingredient? (The less processed, the better)

● How many non-food ingredients (additives) does it contain? (The fewer the better)

● Does it contain some protein?

● Is it relatively low in sugars and carbohydrates?

● Does it contain cheap fats? (vegetable oils, hydrogenated fats)

Ask yourself "What is it going to do for me?"

Protein

The topic of protein can be very confusing; you may have heard we eat too much protein, but I'm becoming more convinced that we probably don't eat enough good quality protein containing the full range of amino acids we need to stay healthy.

It is easiest to think of protein in terms of the obvious sources: meat, fish, eggs, pulses, nuts, seeds and cheese, which generally are made up of 10-25% protein. Many other foods contain protein, but in much smaller quantities.

I am seeing that the simple step of including protein with every meal (and varying our protein each day and over a week) can have quite dramatic effects on energy and mood and may be one of the key missing links when it comes to weight management.

Many protein rich foods provide a wide range of minerals and vitamins, making them nutrient dense. They are our main source of amino acids, which are the building blocks of proteins in our bodies. These proteins form the structures in our bodies (bones, muscles, organs etc) and are also needed to make the body function well with signallers and enzymes.

An important purpose of amino acids is to provide building blocks for neurotransmitters (brain chemicals), which are responsible for our enjoyment of life, positive mood, motivation and interest. We need the full range of amino acids to make neurotransmitters, so it makes sense to eat a variety of different proteins to ensure adequate intake and support mental health.

Animal proteins (meat, fish, eggs) contain all the amino acids human bodies need, while vegetable proteins (nuts, seeds, pulses) provide some of them. It is easier to get enough amino acids with a mixed diet, while more effort is required with the choice to be vegetarian or vegan.

Most adults could probably benefit from between 50 and 80g of protein a day, depending on their weight. Individual needs can increase with illness, injury, stress and intensive exercise.

This means we are aiming for 20-25g of protein each meal.

Some examples of the protein content in common foods are:

● One egg - around 8g protein

● 100g meat or fish - 20-25g protein

● 100g of pulses - 8-10g protein

● 100g nuts and seeds - 20-25g protein

Bear in mind that although nuts and seeds yield a meal's worth of protein per 100g, an average portion is around 30-50g, containing 7-12g protein).

When looking at the protein content of packaged foods, remember to consider the portion size; some snack bars, for example, may announce 'high protein' or 15g per 100g, but if the actual bar is only 35g, it provides far less protein than you might expect, along with a lot of sugar.

I've seen mushrooms and avocadoes described as protein foods when they contain only 3g and 2g per 100g respectively. While they are both nutritious foods, a 100g serving will provide nowhere near the amount needed per meal.

The paragraphs above are to illustrate the fact that many of us are not eating very much protein, and to make the case for including protein more often.

Rather than measure, weigh and count, though, it is much simpler to include some protein every time we eat and concentrate on including a range of proteins over a day and a week.

We've become used to basing our meals around carbohydrates, which tend to be nutrient light and not very satisfying, so might make us eat more food overall. Including protein in a meal slows down the release of sugars from the meal and increases nutrient density, keeping us fuller for longer and helping reduce cravings.

If you are vegan or vegetarian, vary your proteins as much as possible. For vegans plenty of pulses AND nuts and seeds are important, while vegetarians can include eggs and moderate dairy as well.

Sugar and carbohydrates

The message is now quite clear – sugar is the devil. It contributes to weight gain, inflammation, poor cholesterol balance, mood disorders and energy swings and dips. It has connections with cancer and Alzheimer's as well as the more obvious diabetes.

It's not just the pure, white and deadly stuff we should be wary of. We need to recognise that 'healthy' sweeteners such as honey and maple syrup are sugar, too. They may have some nutritional properties but at the end of the day they turn to glucose in the blood and can encourage our desire to eat more sweet foods.

Artificial sweeteners need a mention; they may not have any calories, but the sweetness may fool the body into expecting energy, so when that energy doesn't materialise, you can want to eat more. Aside from that, some have questionable safety.

For many people, it is not clear that all 'simple' carbohydrate foods (bread, pasta, baked goods, rice and so on) turn to sugar/glucose in the blood. The blood has a limit on the amount of glucose it can accommodate, so a consistently high carbohydrate diet makes it harder for the body to manage blood sugar. Too much sugar eventually gets stored as fat and can lead to excess weight and diabetes, but it can also damage cholesterol, blood cells and brain cells, so keeping blood levels balanced is key to good health.

We get 'complex' carbohydrates from more nutrient dense foods like vegetables, fruits, pulses, nuts and seeds. Because these foods have a whole range of nutrients as well as slow-release carbohydrates, they are a better choice than nutrient light simple carbs.

Taking in lots of simple carbs with most meals could raise blood sugar levels too high, too quickly. When the body responds by lowering blood sugar it can lead to a roller coaster of mood, energy, brain function and cravings. Watch the simple carbs and have in mind that they are basically the same as sugar in the blood.

There is a lot of debate about whether carbohydrate-dense foods are a valuable part of our diet, and many nutritional thinkers regard them as superfluous at best, harmful at worst. I believe most of the foods we think of as carbohydrates are less nutrient dense than protein and vegetables.

Carbs are cheap and plentiful, but in today's climate of non-food/fake food (i.e. highly processed products with little original nutrition) we can't afford to regard standard carbs as a useful food.

Our inactive lifestyles may also reduce our need for carbohydrates – most of us no longer have physical jobs either in the home or workplace, so we don't need quick releasing carbohydrates; our energy needs are so different from what they were even 30 years ago that we really need to look at what we're eating and assess what is best for us in modern times.

Eating slow-release complex carbohydrates along with protein can help us manage blood sugar levels and consequently improve energy, mood, brain function and general wellbeing. Simply focussing on good quality protein and vegetables helps us naturally reduce our carbs while increasing nutrient density, without consciously thinking about it. This is much easier than **trying** to reduce carbohydrates.

Retraining taste buds

Food has become sweeter and sweeter – even vegetables are being bred with less bitter flavours to make them more palatable. Why?! These are the very properties which help us resist sweet foods.

Sugar, and therefore sweetness, is not doing us any favours; I think we need to retrain our taste buds and reset our expectations so that sweetness is a rarity. When food is made with less care, it's easy to season it with sugar and salt, so when you really taste it, there is no depth of flavour. Take away the sugar, use herbs and spices and a moderate amount of good quality sea salt, and notice just how much flavour your food has.

Fats

At last, fat is being recognised as essential for good health. I believe our focus should be on quality rather than quantity. Think about how much the fat or oil you are using has been altered from its original state:

● If it's clear and golden, it's likely to be highly processed, damaged and probably not a good idea.

● If it contains anything other than the original oil/fat plus a bit of salt (preferably sea salt), avoid it.

● If it comes from an animal which is intensively reared and fed mainly on grains and soya, give it a miss.

My advice is to stick with unadulterated fats – butter, olive oil*, coconut oil and fat from naturally reared animals. Leave out processed vegetable fats, which are not only heat-treated and damaged, but have higher quantities of potentially inflammatory Omega 6 oils. Eat fat in its wholefood form in nuts, seeds, fish, wild and grass-fed animals, eggs, olives, avocadoes and so on. This way you are including the other nutrients needed to help you process these fats for use in the body. Food is very clever – unadulterated, it comes in packages of nutrients which help us to make the best of its properties. Remove any part of it and it no longer works in the same way.

*There is much confusion about whether we should cook with olive oil. As the Mediterranean diet is seen as one of the healthiest and uses copious amounts, it's probably ok. The antioxidants in extra virgin olive oil may also help limit any damage from cooking.

I would suggest that you avoid sizzling food; cooking it gently is less likely to damage both the food and the oil. However, if you want to cook at higher temperatures, saturated fat is best, as the heat won't damage it. Butter, coconut oil and animal fat are saturated fats.

Maximising intake from plants

It is important to incorporate lots of different plant foods into everyone's diet. The term 'plant-based' appears to exclude the idea of eating animal products and therefore might miss the attention of many people. I suggest 'plant-focussed' might highlight the need for all of us to eat lots of plants, regardless of philosophy.

It can be fun to try and use as many different plant foods in meals as possible. These include vegetables, fruits, seeds, nuts, pulses, herbs and spices. I'm happiest when I get to around 10 per meal, which isn't always possible (and that's fine), but some examples might be:

● Breakfast: blackberries, apples, four types of seeds, walnuts, grated turmeric and ginger, cacao powder or nibs, which makes 10.

● Lunch: Lettuce, rocket, watercress, carrot, beetroot, avocado, olives, sprouted seeds, broccoli, seaweed sprinkles, hummus, which makes 15 including the beans, garlic, lemon and tahini in the hummus.

● Dinner: Stew with onions, leeks, sweet potato, mushroom, herbs, green veg, making 6.

Having herbs, spices, jars of seeds, dried seaweed sprinkles, tahini, nut butters, lemon dressing, olives, jars of artichokes, frozen peas, salad veg, root veg and sprouted seeds around helps a lot. It can be fun to see just how many different ingredients you can include in a meal. It doesn't need to be huge quantities, and I really believe that little bits here and there can make a big difference.

Aim for a minimum of 40 different plant foods over a week, but don't stop there!

Variety

The more different ingredients you put in your dishes, the more nutrient dense they are. It could be argued that the lack of diversity in our diet has contributed to our many current health issues. The diversity of gut bacteria, for example, is widely recognised as an indicator of health. Simply by increasing the variety of plant foods in your diet you encourage diversity in your gut bacteria, and this is understood to have wide ranging effects on all aspects of health, including weight and mental wellbeing.

Variety is one of the keys to good health; by incorporating many different foods in your daily and weekly diet, you tick lots of nutritional boxes – vitamins, minerals, antioxidants, amino acids, essential fats and the properties of herbs and spices.

Concentrating on eating a rainbow of colours in your vegetables and fruits is a great way of ensuring you get a wide range of nutrients.

Different coloured foods contain different minerals, vitamins and antioxidants, so aim to cover the rainbow each day. It has the added benefit of making your food look attractive, making it more of a pleasure to create and eat.

Gluten and grains

Gluten is a protein present in wheat, barley and rye, and in recent years going gluten free has become more common. It has been shown to damage the gut lining, which can lead to health problems, even in people who are not coeliac. Many people feel better avoiding gluten; effects can range from improving digestion, migraines, mood, weight, joint pain and more. The gluten free trend is often seen as a fad, but the numbers of people who report an improvement by removing gluten from their diet cannot be ignored. Personally, gluten causes low mood within 24 hours and long term intake creates joint pain, so for me it's a no-brainer.

One thing to bear in mind if you decide to go gluten free, is that it's important to include plenty of prebiotic fibre in your diet – this is the stuff which feeds the 'good' bacteria. Simply upping your vegetable and plant consumption and concentrating on variety will do this.

Remember that vegetables, fruits, meat, fish, nuts, seeds and pulses are all naturally gluten free!

Grains are more of a grey area; good quality whole grains may contain some useful nutrients. However, they are still mostly carbohydrate foods, and personally I would rather eat more vegetables than grains because they contain more nutrients.

I hope this section helps explain key elements of my thinking around nutrition. At the end of the day, choose real food, prepare it yourself and treat yourself, your friends and family to better health.

 Index

About me

I'm a cook, not a chef, and have only recently come to understand the difference – the most liberating of which is that you don't have to follow the rules! I was lucky enough to have a mum who let me experiment in the kitchen from a very early age, so I've always loved cooking.

I qualified as a Nutritional Therapist in 2011. I have developed my own Nutrition in a Nutshell course, which aims to explain the basic principles of good nutrition alongside practical demonstrations and tasters. I run cooking workshops, see clients and give talks and presentations. Tina's Kitchen started in 2014 after my market stall selling salads and healthy lunches showed there was a need for this kind of food.

I trained as a teacher and Bowen therapist, ran the local farmers' market, wrote the Friendly Vegetable Book and was involved in setting up Green Wheels Day and the Artists' and Makers' Fair. I am married with three grown up daughters.

I've had a few health problems including severe PMS, arthritis, breast cancer and osteoporosis, all of which have fuelled my interest in using diet as a way of improving my health. Along the way I've said goodbye to lifelong constipation, headaches and low mood. I'm still a work in progress and live in hope of a healthy and active older age.

Thank you

My mum for letting me loose in the kitchen as a child.

My husband, Alan, and daughters, Hannah, Rosie and Alice, for their support and faith in me.

My wonderful customers, who've given me the confidence to write this book, because they seem to like my food!

My landlady, Collette, who enabled me to grow Tina's Kitchen organically.

Lewes Friday Market for giving me stall space and getting me started.

The lovely people who've worked for me over the last three years.

Julie for checking and re-checking the text for me.

Tony for his patience and creativity designing this book.

Also to everyone else who has supported, encouraged and nagged me to get on with finishing this book!